Contents

1 | Introduction

What is design and communication?

Designing is an everyday activity. Decorating a room and deciding where the furniture should be placed is designing. So is planning a party, or planting flowers in the garden. When we try to solve a practical problem in a systematic way, we are designing.

Almost everything that is made has been designed. We all use hundreds of man-made things, from buildings to paper clips, every day. A chair that is uncomfortable, or looks ugly, or breaks easily is badly designed. A well-designed pen should, among other things, write clearly, be reliable and easy to use.

Communication is important at all stages of the design process. Sketches, notes, models, drawings and computer graphics are some of the ways we communicate ideas and information to other people.

Information is also needed by people who are going to make, use or sell a product. This information may, for example, be in the form of a working drawing, an advertisement, a photograph or an 'instructions for use' leaflet.

Chapters 2–5 of this book will help you learn about designing objects. Chapter 6–8 concentrate on ways of communicating general information. Chapter 9 (computer aided design) can be used during any suitable activity, and Chapter 10 contains suggestions for complete projects.

ACTIVITY

Make a list of things at home or at school which you think have been well designed. Make another list of things you think were badly designed. Give at least one reason for your opinion in each case.

Compare your lists with others. How did you decide whether something was designed well or not?

4

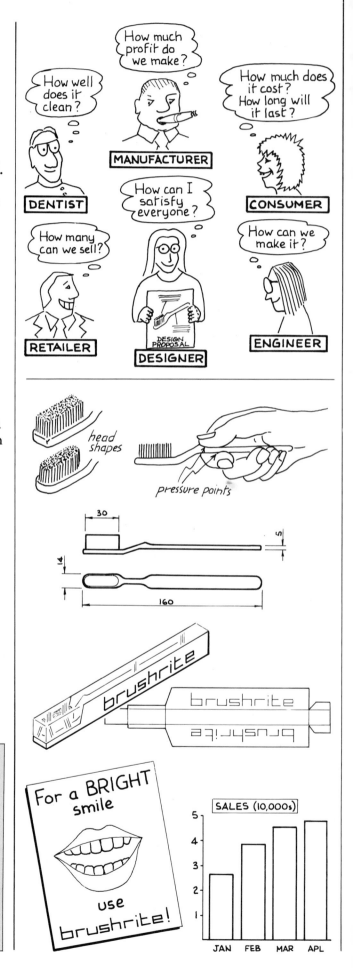

What you need to use this book
(See Chapter 5 for model making needs.)

Pencils – grades B and 2H
A good quality soft pencil rubber

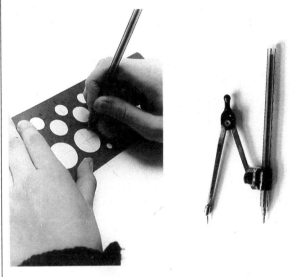

Black ballpoint pen – slim case, parallel nib. Can be used with circle and ellipse templates (left) and with pencil compasses (right)

Bank paper (a thin, strong paper) A4 size
Square grid sheet – 5mm squares
Isometric grid sheet – 5mm matrix
Cartridge paper A3 and A4 sizes
Draughting tape

A range of felt tip markers with a medium tip size
A range of colouring pencils

Drawing board with parallel motion or T-square
Set squares
Draughting ruler
Compasses
Protractor
Spring clips for holding paper
Cleaning cloth

The design process

The diagram below shows the design process divided into stages. Study the diagram, and you should find that you are already familiar with some of the activities described. The design process is really a natural and common sense way of solving many practical, everyday problems.

Some teachers may use slightly different words for the stages, but the meanings will be similar to those described below. You should agree with your teacher which words you are going to use, to avoid confusion.

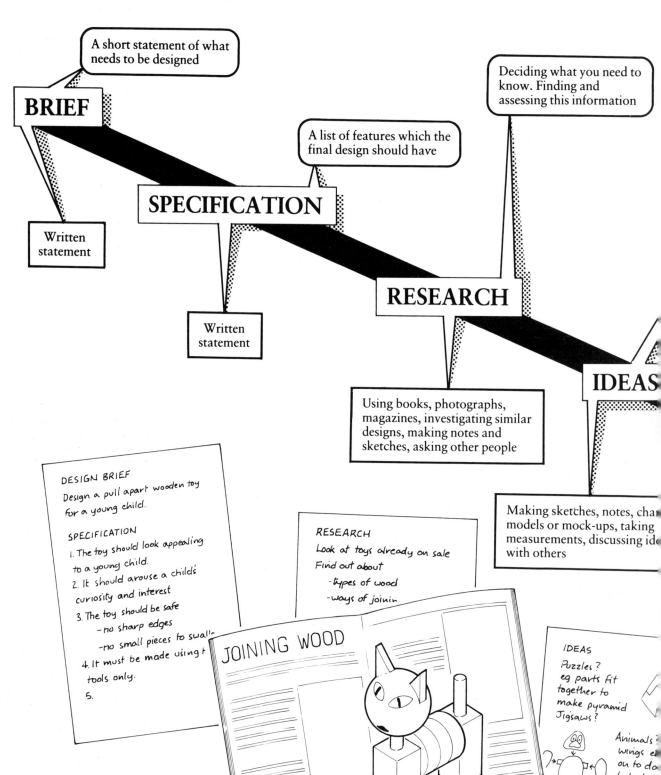

A short statement of what needs to be designed

BRIEF

Written statement

A list of features which the final design should have

SPECIFICATION

Written statement

Deciding what you need to know. Finding and assessing this information

RESEARCH

Using books, photographs, magazines, investigating similar designs, making notes and sketches, asking other people

IDEAS

Making sketches, notes, cha[...] models or mock-ups, taking measurements, discussing id[...] with others

DESIGN BRIEF
Design a pull apart wooden toy for a young child.

SPECIFICATION
1. The toy should look appealing to a young child.
2. It should arouse a child's curiosity and interest
3. The toy should be safe
   – no sharp edges
   – no small pieces to swall[...]
4. It must be made using h[...] tools only.
5.

RESEARCH
Look at toys already on sale
Find out about
  – types of wood
  – ways of joinin[...]

JOINING WOOD

IDEAS
Puzzles?
eg parts fit together to make pyramid
Jigsaws?

Animals[...]
wings [...]
on to do[...]
to body
(duck, to[...]

A design problem starts with a **brief** like the one shown below. As a designer, you may be given a brief, or you may decide for yourself what the brief is to be.

You will sometimes need to work on your own, and at other times as part of a team.

You will need to plan your activities so that you complete each task in the time available. Designers in industry have to work to deadlines, too.

As you work through the design process, you will often find that you have to go back to a previous stage to solve a problem. This is quite normal. Your progress will be rather like a train shunting backwards and forwards, but eventually arriving at its destination!

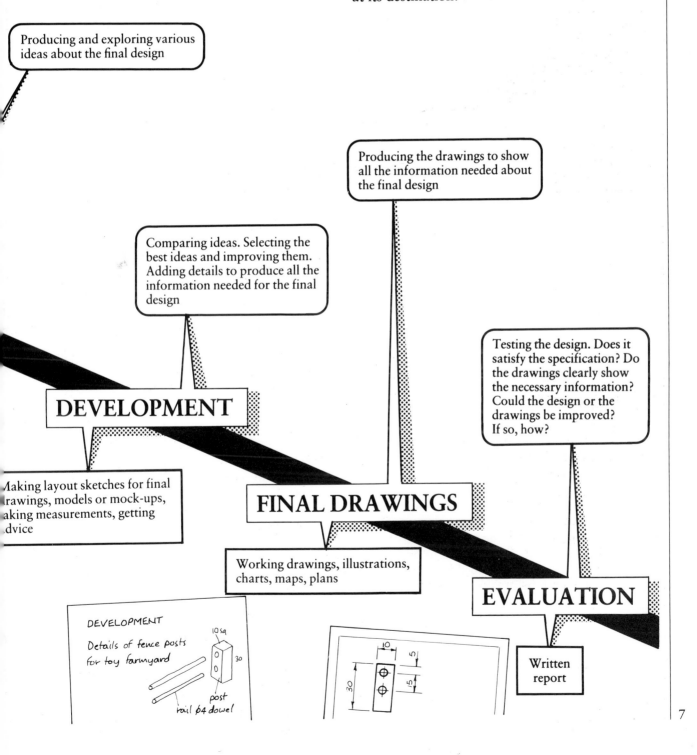

Producing and exploring various ideas about the final design

Producing the drawings to show all the information needed about the final design

Comparing ideas. Selecting the best ideas and improving them. Adding details to produce all the information needed for the final design

Testing the design. Does it satisfy the specification? Do the drawings clearly show the necessary information? Could the design or the drawings be improved? If so, how?

DEVELOPMENT

Making layout sketches for final drawings, models or mock-ups, taking measurements, getting advice

FINAL DRAWINGS

Working drawings, illustrations, charts, maps, plans

EVALUATION

Written report

DEVELOPMENT

Details of fence posts for toy farmyard

10 sq

30

post

rail φ4 dowel

10

5

30

15

DESIGN BRIEF
Design a puppet theatre which can be used with string or glove puppets

SPECIFICATION
① Operator must be hidden from the audience
② Operator must be able to reach under the floor
③ Theatre needs an open top for using string puppets
④ Floor needs to be removable for using string puppets
⑤ Front of theatre needs an attractive, exciting appearance
⑥

RESEARCH
① Dimensions —

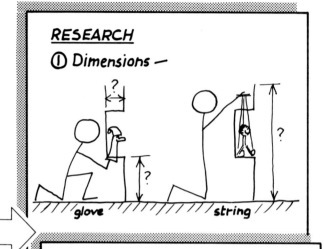

glove   string

IDEAS
① Shape and construction —

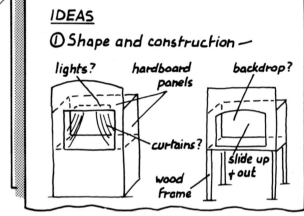

lights?   hardboard panels   backdrop?

curtains?

wood frame   slide up + out

Design in action

Pat's CDT teacher had given her group a **brief** for designing a puppet theatre.

Pat thought hard about the brief and started to write a **specification**. She could think of only five points, but left space for more in case she needed to add to the list later.

Her **research** included finding out what materials were available and how much time was allowed to finish the design.

Pat then started to sketch some **ideas** about the basic shape and construction of the theatre. This helped her to think about the problems involved. She soon discovered that she needed to find out some important dimensions. So she had to do some more research before going any further.

Pat sketched several more ideas, bearing in mind these measurements. She knew that first ideas are not always the best ones, and that it is important to explore alternatives. She wrote questions and comments on her sketches to help her to compare them. Several times she re-read her specification to remind herself exactly what she was trying to achieve.

She chose a basic design that seemed sturdy, attractive and easy to make. She realised that these factors should be included in the specification, and added them to her original list.

Pat decided to test this basic design by making a full size **model** of the front panel and stage, using corrugated card from old cartons. After trying this model with actual puppets (with the help of a friend) she thought the stage was too narrow, and decided to make it wider.

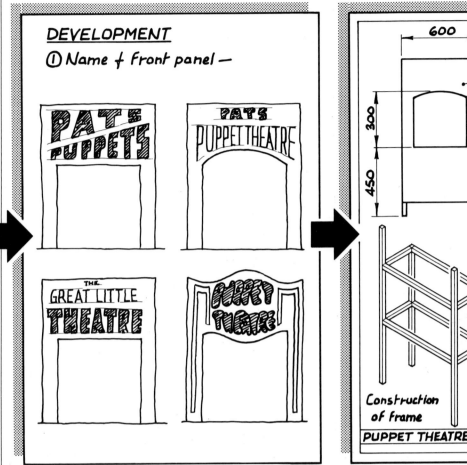

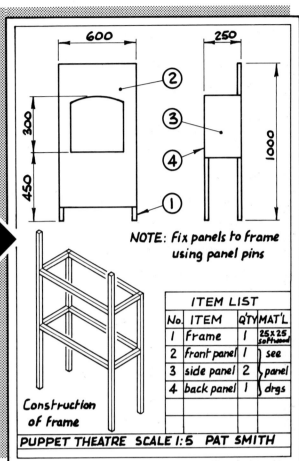

The next step was to **develop** this basic design by sketching details such as the front panel. After deciding these final details, Pat drew a **working drawing** of her final design. This was drawn to scale using drawing instruments. It shows all the information needed to make the finished article.

Pat's teacher then asked her group to produce an **illustration** advertising the puppet theatre. This involved sketches and ideas, before drawing the final illustration.

Pat's CDT group then got together to **evaluate** their designs, and the effectiveness of their drawings, by discussing and comparing them.

ACTIVITIES

1 What other features could Pat have added to her specification?

2 How would you go about finding out the measurements that Pat needed to know?

3 What other selling points could be included in the advertisement?

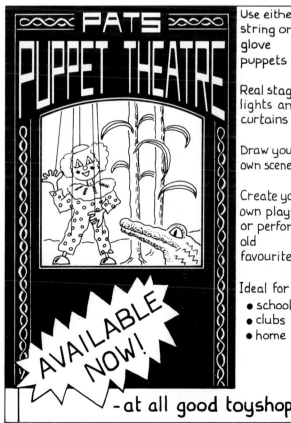

2 | 2-D design sketching

Using a grid

Designers need to be able to draw freehand sketches quickly, confidently and with reasonable accuracy.

Many things that are designed and made have simple shapes. This makes them easy to draw using square grid paper as a guide.

Use A4 size 5mm square grid paper, 'bank' paper and a grade B pencil. Place the bank paper over the grid paper and line up the edges carefully.

If possible, use masking tape or paper clips to fix both sheets together at two opposite corners. Alternatively, you can fix both sheets to your drawing board with spring clips.

When drawing, use the grid as a guide and trace each line with one movement – do not 'stroke' the lines. Press evenly on your pencil but not too hard. Do *not* use a ruler to draw lines.

It is easier to draw long lines if you move your paper around so you are drawing from left to right and slightly upwards, as in the photograph (or from right to left if you are left handed). This will give you the best control over your pencil. You do not need to do this for short lines.

When you rub out a line, press down firmly with your finger tips each side of the rubber, or the paper will tear.

As soon as you can trace accurately from the grid, you can start producing your own design sketches.

Design sketches are for **trying out ideas.** Always produce several ideas so you can compare them. Try to think as you draw.

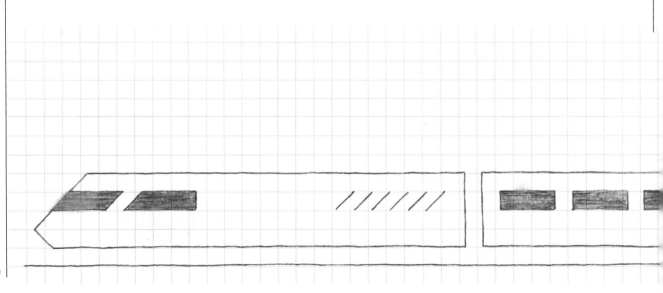

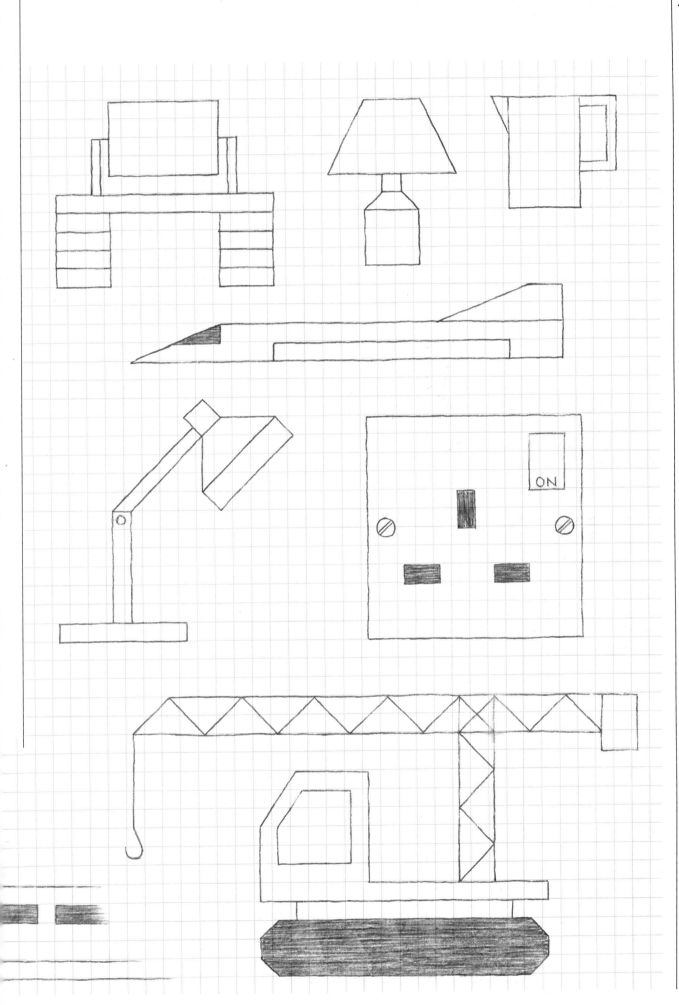

Colouring with pencils

To use a coloured pencil (or an ordinary lead pencil) hold it almost flat, as in the photograph. Move the pencil quickly left and right, and gradually towards you, until the area is covered.

Press lightly for a pale colour, and harder for a darker colour.

Use the side of your forefinger, or a ruler, to stop the pencil going over the edge of the area you are colouring.

For a large area, colour about half way across, then turn the paper around and colour from the opposite edge in the same way.

Try to colour evenly. You will need to sharpen your pencil frequently.

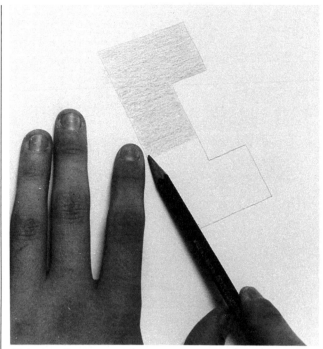

Using a colouring pencil

Colouring with felt markers

Markers give a dense, even colour when properly used. This takes practice, especially when using dark colours.

Hold the marker as you would for writing. Cover the area, once only, from side to side and down as in the photograph.

Move the marker deliberately but not too slowly. Do not lift the marker from the paper until you have finished.

Do not touch the ink until it is dry.

To cover large areas you need markers with extra large tips.

Using a ballpoint pen

Drawing over an outline in ink makes it stand out more than a pencil line.

You should only 'ink in' sketches after you have finished any necessary colouring. It is almost impossible to make changes or correct mistakes properly.

Press evenly and move the pen slowly. Try to start and finish exactly on the ends of each line.

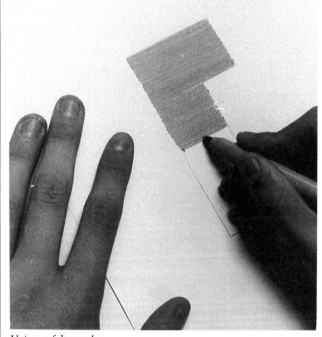

Using a felt marker

ACTIVITIES

1 Using a square grid and bank paper, draw some simple rectangular shapes like those shown.

Colour these shapes evenly in different colours using colouring pencils.

Draw similar shapes on another sheet of bank paper. Colour these in different colours using felt markers.

2 Copy or trace some of the sketches from the previous page.

Look at other objects with simple shapes, and draw them in a similar way. Keep your sketches simple – do not add small details.

Colour your sketches, using colouring pencils or felt markers as you think most suitable.

Draw over the outlines using a ballpoint pen.

3 Computer characters are designed on a grid of 8 × 8 squares.

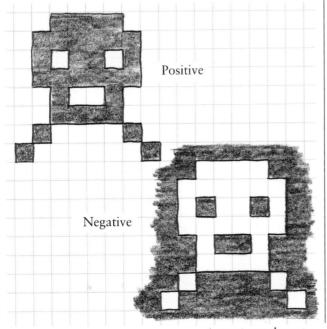

Positive

Negative

A computer character

Draw at least twelve 8 × 8 square outlines on a sheet of bank paper. Sketch and colour two ideas each for the following characters:

- an elephant
- a tortoise
- a person walking
- a jet aircraft
- a plant in a flower pot
- a design of your own choice.

Discuss your finished designs. Which are the most recognisable?

4 Sketch an outline plan of your graphics room, showing the positions of the drawing boards and other furniture.

Write in capitals the names of people at each drawing board position.

Colour the floor area evenly in a light colour. This will make the furniture stand out.

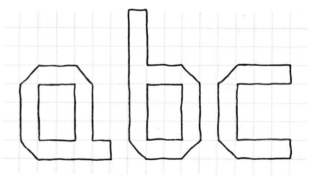

5 Your name is to be displayed at a design exhibition.

Sketch the letters of your name using a square grid, similar to the example shown. Produce at least two alternative designs, and draw a border around each.

On another sheet of bank paper, trace your best design carefully using a ruler. Colour either the letters or the background, using one colour only.

ACTIVITIES

6 A basic calculator with four functions needs sixteen keys. List the keys.

Complete this specification for a basic calculator:

a The display should be easy to read.
b The shape should . . .
c The keys should . . .
d . . . ?

Look at different calculators and discuss these points.

Draw several design sketches for a basic four-function calculator. There are several ways of arranging sixteen keys. How you arrange them will affect the shape of the calculator.

How many digits can a calculator display? Make sure you can fit these in your display window.

7 Imagine you are going to make your own desk to use at home. Write a specification for your desk. Here is a guide:

List things you would **do** at your desk (e.g. writing, drawing, computer games) and things you would **store** in it (e.g. paper, letters, cassette tapes).

Add other desirable features, e.g. the desk should look interesting, it should have a large work area.

On one sheet of bank paper, sketch four versions (front views) of what your desk could look like. Make notes on each sketch saying where you would store various items.

Select the version which fits your specification best. Print FINAL DESIGN in large letters under this sketch.

8 Mazes are fascinating puzzles. Here is a simple way of solving most mazes, called the 'right hand rule'.

Enter the maze and keep walking, always touching the right hand wall. Try this on the maze shown.

Sketch your own maze inside a 12 × 12 square on the grid. There must be only on solution – a difficult one!

Measure the time taken for several classmates to solve your maze, using the table shown.

Calculate the average time taken. What does this tell you about your maze?

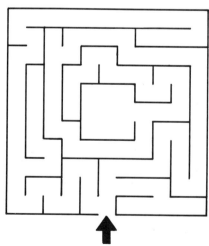

NAME	TIME (secs)	
Justin		Average
Joan		time taken
Darren		= TOTAL
Isobel		4
TOTAL		= ?

ACTIVITIES

9 The sketches below are made up of straight lines, circles and parts of circles called **arcs**. Note how the circles fit the squares on the grid.

To draw small circles, keep the heel of your hand on the paper and draw the circle in one movement of your pencil.

Large circles are best drawn a quarter circle at a time. Turn the paper around to a convenient position for each arc.

Practise drawing circles of different sizes, and copying some of the designs below.

Try to discover other patterns using circles and arcs. Several patterns can often be made from the same shape by colouring different areas.

Sketch your initials or your name, using arcs for some of the lines.

Sketch a series of ideas for:

- a tractor
- a moon buggy
- a model railway layout.

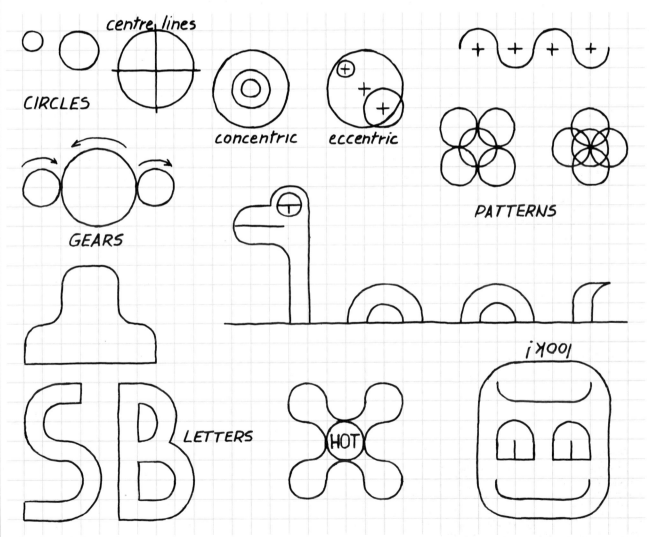

Sketching circles and arcs

3 | 3-D design sketching

There are several ways of drawing solid objects on paper. They are called **projections** because a drawing is rather like a shadow of an object projected on to the ground. The shadow shows the shape of the object, but in two dimensions rather than three.

Orthographic projection

We often want to draw views of the side, ends, or top of an object. Only these views show us the exact shape and size to make the object.

The drawing below shows three views together.

This kind of drawing is called **orthographic projection**.

Use horizontal grid lines to line up heights between the elevations.

Use vertical grid lines to line up widths between the front elevation and the plan.

Orthographic projection is usually used for working drawings. Single elevation or plan views can also be useful in design sketching.

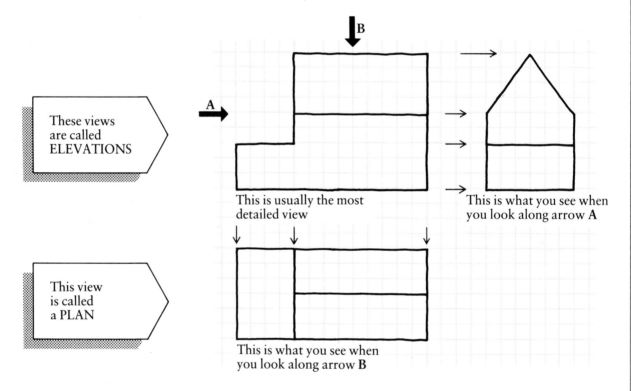

These views are called ELEVATIONS

This is usually the most detailed view

This is what you see when you look along arrow **A**

This view is called a PLAN

This is what you see when you look along arrow **B**

Oblique projection

Sometimes we want to show the general appearance of an object. This is called a **pictorial view**.

This drawing shows a kind of pictorial view called **oblique projection**.

Oblique views are easy to draw, provided the surfaces going away from you have simple shapes, and the front surface is vertical.

Start by drawing one of the orthographic views on a square grid. Then draw the 'front to back' edges diagonally from the corners. Finally, draw the back edges.

The diagonal edges should be drawn shorter than their true length. As a guide, draw one square diagonal for every two square sides.

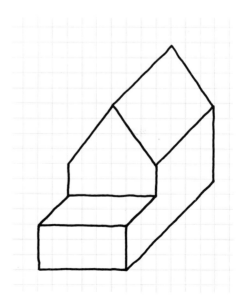

Isometric projection

The drawing opposite shows another kind of pictorial view called **isometric projection**.

Isometric views are easy to draw using an isometric grid sheet. These have lines going in three directions, as shown. Compare this grid to the square grid. Each square has become a diamond – a square seen from an angle.

The edges of the object which are on the grid lines are drawn their **true length** – their scale length on the actual object. There are three lines in the final drawing which are **not** their true length. Can you see which they are?

To draw an isometric view, start at the bottom corner, and follow the stages shown. Note that vertical lines remain vertical.

You can measure only along the grid lines. To find the top of the roof, measure (or count the squares) along the lines shown by the arrows.

Both isometric and oblique views of an object can be drawn from different viewpoints. Some alternative viewpoints are shown below.

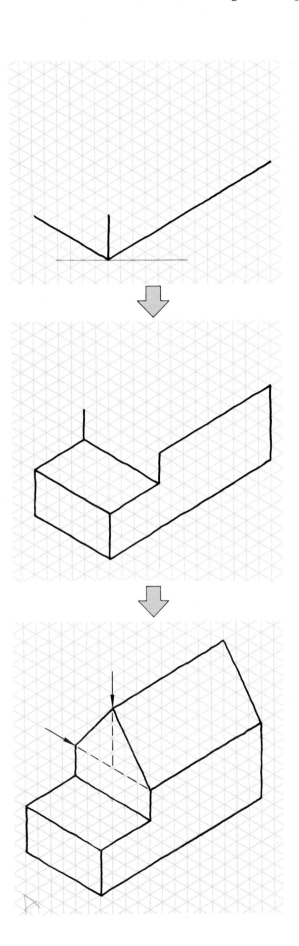

Alternative viewpoints

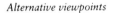
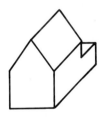
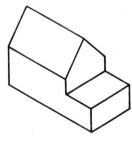
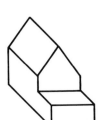
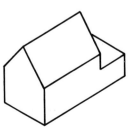

Lines and shading

Here are some ways of making your drawings appear more solid and realistic. Study the effect that each gives.

You can use all these methods on freehand design sketches as shown here, or on finished presentation drawings (see Chapter 4).

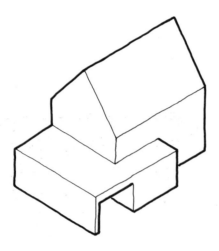

Thick and thin lines

Draw extra thick lines where they are next to empty space. This adds an impression of depth.

Use a lead pencil or ballpoint pen.

Shading according to light source

Shade surfaces facing away from the source of light more heavily.

Use a lead pencil, coloured pencil or different shades of the same colour felt marker.

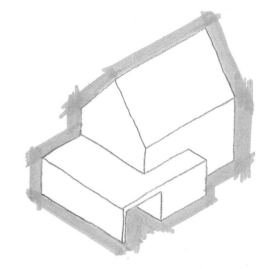

Background shading

This gives emphasis to a white object drawn on white paper. Leave the outside of the shading ragged as shown.

Use a coloured pencil or felt tip marker.

You can use these and other techniques together to show in more detail the construction of an object and the materials used.

Representing materials

Wood

Look at some wooden objects. The end grain consists of arcs, and the side grain consists of wavy lines, sometimes containing knots.

Imagine a fast flowing stream, with an occasional small rock sticking out of the water. Side grain 'flows' in the same way, and this is how you should draw your wavy lines.

You can use a lead or colouring pencil, or a ballpoint pen. Make the lines very thin. If using a colouring pencil you can also shade according to the light source.

Polished metal and plastic

Polished surfaces reflect large areas of light. The sketch opposite shows glossy coloured letters. To show this effect, shade *unevenly* spaced stripes diagonally using a colouring pencil.

If you then cut out the letters and mount them on dark paper, they look even more effective.

A similar method is shown for the metal box. Use blue for steel, and light brown for brass or gold. Note how the angle of the stripes is different on each surface.

Rubber, concrete and textured plastic

An effective way to represent these materials is to apply **stipple** using a ballpoint pen.

Dab the pen repeatedly on the paper lightly and quickly. Apply plenty of dots on surfaces which are in shade, and few or none at all on surfaces which face the light.

It is tiring to apply stipple to large areas. Film transfer is obtainable which is rubbed down and trimmed with a craft knife, but it is rather expensive.

Glass and clear plastic

Drawing **razor lines** is an effective way to represent these.

Use a pencil or a ballpoint pen, and a ruler. Flick the point quickly and lightly across the paper, so that the lines taper in thickness.

Draw two or three groups of closely spaced razor lines. Only a few lines are needed in each group – too many will spoil the effect.

ACTIVITIES

1 Sketch these two isometric views of a small matchbox, using an isometric grid. Colour the top yellow, the sides black and all other surfaces blue, using felt markers.

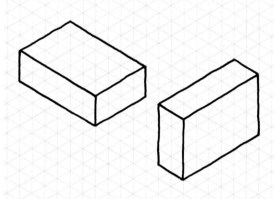

Sketch the same matchbox from as many different viewpoints as you can, and colour them as above. There are twelve possible isometric views.

Try sketching the same matchbox partly open. See how many oblique views of it you can draw. Looking at a real matchbox will help you.

2 Sketch orthographic and isometric views of a full size matchbox as shown. Use the correct grid for each.

On another sheet of bank paper, sketch and colour four ideas for a matchbox label.

SIDE

END

PLAN

ISOMETRIC

Draw and colour your best label design on the plan and the isometric view. Colour or shade the remainder of the drawing as realistically as you can.

3 Sketch a city from your imagination, using an isometric grid.

Start with the buildings in the foreground, and make them smaller the further away they are.

Shade the buildings as if the sun (the source of light) were on the right in your drawing.

4 Sketch several ideas for the front view of your initials. Make them 10 units high on a square grid, and use straight lines only.

Redraw your best idea in oblique projection, based on the front view. You can use this sketch to trace off as many other copies as you need.

Make different versions of these letters look like wood, polished plastic and textured plastic.

ACTIVITIES

5 Below are two views of various objects in orthographic projection.

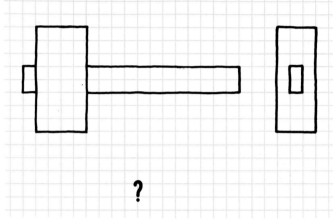

?

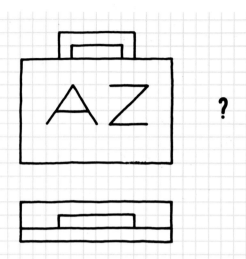

?

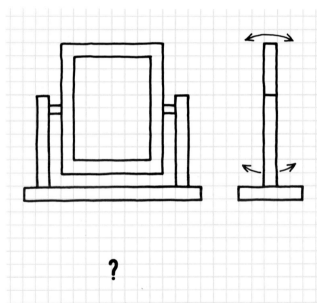

?

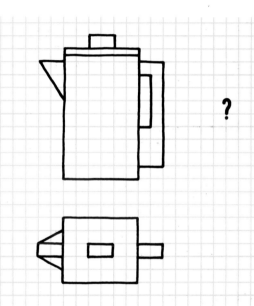

?

Copy these using a square grid, and draw the missing views.

Sketch the objects in isometric projection. Practice using thick and thin lines, and background shading on your sketches. Trace as many versions of each as you need.

Produce some versions showing each object made from a suitable material.

ACTIVITIES

6 The drawing below shows various objects in isometric projection.

Sketch some of these objects using an isometric grid, but from a different viewpoint, for example, looking up at the aeroplane flying left.

Shade each sketch as if the source of light were from the top right of each object. You can use more than one colour if you wish, for example, tractor body yellow, tracks grey.

Using a square grid, sketch three views of each object in orthographic projection.

7 Try sketching other objects with simple shapes. They can be from real life or from your imagination. Here are some examples:

- a cassette recorder
- a space station
- a sewing machine
- a computer and monitor
- a robot
- kitchen scales.

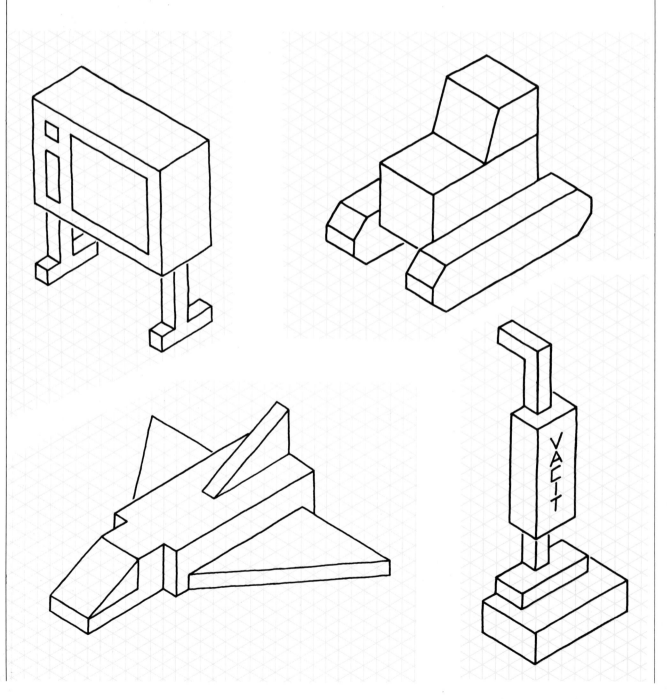

ACTIVITIES

8 The drawings below are of impossible objects. The box and the waterfall (see photograph) were designed by a famous Dutch artist, M.C. Escher.

Drawings are two dimensional **representations** of three dimensional objects. They seem to have depth because in our minds we are trying to see the real objects. If the objects are impossible, we get confused!

Try sketching some of the drawings below.

Can you colour the two-pronged trident and the projecting groove? Your teacher may offer you a large reward if you can.

Copy and then complete the waterfall drawing started below. Use the photograph as a guide. Add the water and any other details you want.

M.C. Escher, *Waterfall*, lithograph, 1961

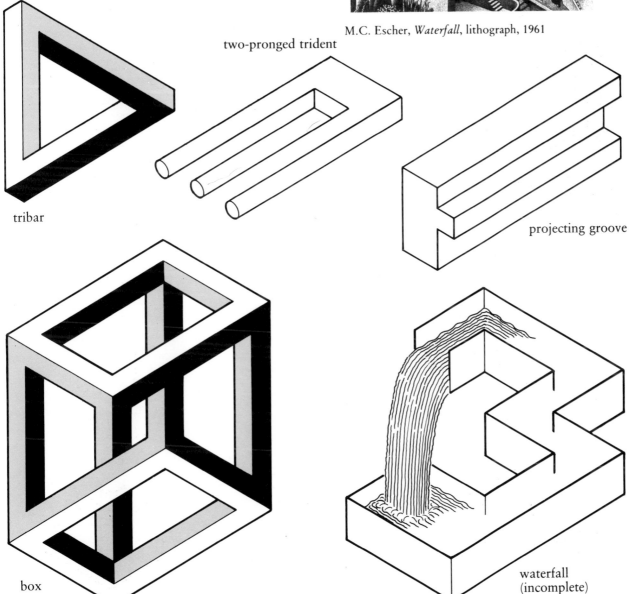

two-pronged trident

tribar

projecting groove

box

waterfall
(incomplete)

Impossible objects?

23

Circles and cylinders

A circle fits into a square like this. Note the centre lines.

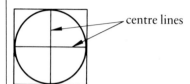

centre lines

To draw a cylinder in **oblique** projection it must face forwards. The ends remain as circles. Start by drawing feint centre lines and axis as shown.

A circle seen at an angle appears as an **ellipse**.

An ellipse is a shape in between a circle and a straight line.

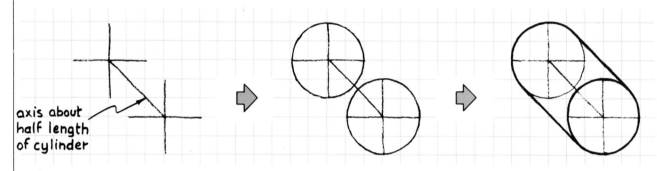

axis about half length of cylinder

A cylinder drawn in **isometric** projection can face in any direction along the grid lines. The ends

become ellipses. Start by drawing feint centre lines and square ends as shown.

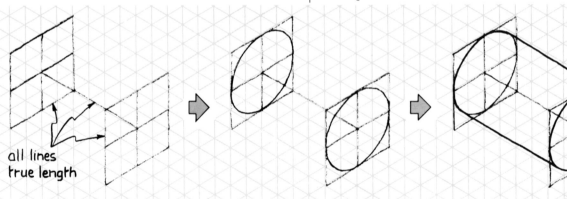

all lines true length

With practice, you will not need to draw the square ends or the centre lines. They are already on the grid – you just need to see where they are. Corner marks can help.

Drawing an object as a 'wire frame' often helps you to see the finished outline.

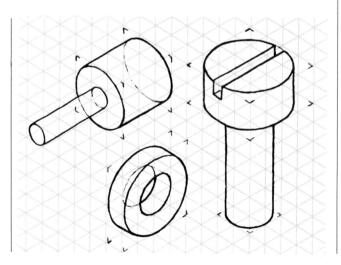

You can use the thick and thin line technique, and shading on cylinders.

Shade **gradually** away from the source of light.

Build up more complex objects by combining cylinders and boxes.

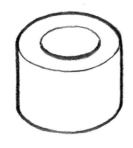
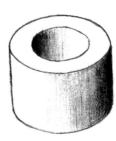

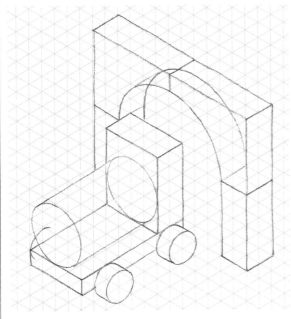
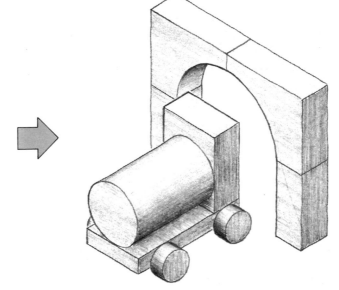

To draw single objects based on cylinders such as containers, use a vertical grid line as an axis.

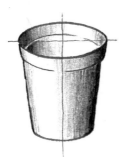

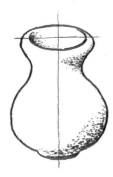

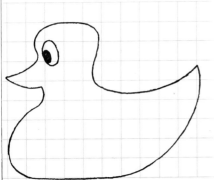
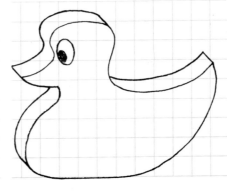

Freehand shapes can be drawn on a square grid. Such shapes can easily be redrawn in oblique or isometric projection, by plotting points at intervals on the grid.

ACTIVITIES

1 Sketch the object shown using an isometric grid. Start with the cube, and add each cylinder in turn.

Shade your drawing with the light source in the position shown. Use one coloured pencil only.

As a further challenge, could you add three cylinders fixed to the hidden sides of the cube?

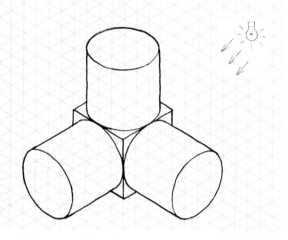

2 The photograph shows a child's peg and hammer toy.

Sketch a plan view of a similar toy on a square grid to work out the positions of the pegs.

Use this plan to sketch an isometric view of the complete toy. Draw a suitable hammer lying beside it.

Shade the drawing using bright colours.

3 Here is an incomplete elevation and plan of a radio cassette player. Copy these views twice the size shown and sketch an isometric view.

To complete the design sketches add the following items:

- two speakers and a cassette door on the front
- round control knobs for on/off/volume, balance and tone on the top.

Make the various parts of the radio cassette look as though they are made from suitable materials.

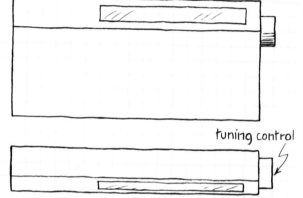

tuning control

4 The photograph shows a wooden bird table and box for mounting on a tall pole in a garden.

Sketch at least two ideas, using both orthographic and isometric projection, for a similar table. Add wood grain to your sketches, and notes on the design features.

The box should have a sloping roof and suitable access for the birds. What other features should the box and table have?

ACTIVITIES

5 The sketches below show some wooden parts of a construction toy. When correctly fitted together, these parts make a model hippopotamus.

The name and quantity of each part is shown ('off' means quantity).

Produce an isometric drawing of the complete hippopotamus. You will find it useful to sketch a side elevation first.

Choose the position of a source of light, and shade the finished drawing in a suitable colour.

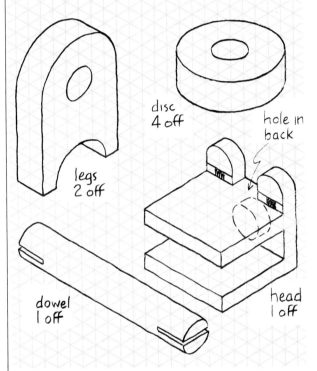

Toy hippopotamus parts

6 Produce two design sketches of containers to store each of the following:

- sugar
- liquid detergent
- antiseptic cream.

Think carefully how each type of container will be used. For example, to extract the sugar a spoon will probably be used, so the container will need a wide lid.

Include suitable brand names on your containers.

7 A tray is needed to carry six hot drinks in disposable cups safely. The cups are to sit in holes in the tray, which is to be a plastic moulding.

Complete this specification for the tray:
a The tray must hold the cups securely.
b The tray must catch any spilt liquid.
c . . . ?
Produce several design sketches for the shape of the tray and the positions of the holes. State what you think are the advantages and disadvantages of each idea.

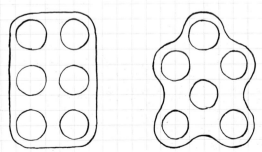

Tray layouts

4 | Working drawings and illustrations

Using instruments

Drawing instruments are used for producing accurate work, such as scale working drawings and illustrations.

If drawn on tracing paper or draughting film, the drawings are called **originals**, and prints (copies) can be made from them on a dyeline printer. In school, cartridge paper is usually used.

The basic instruments are a drawing board with a parallel motion or T-square, two set squares, a ruler, compasses, rubber and grade 2H pencil.

Wipe the set squares and sliding bar or T-square regularly with a cloth. They tend to get dirty very quickly. Sharpen your pencil frequently.

Line up the bottom edge of your drawing sheet with the T-square, and clip or tape it to the board.

Set squares

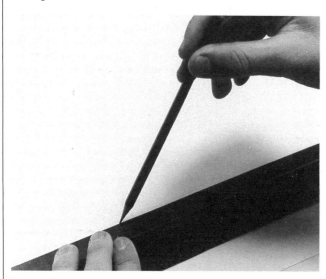

To draw feint lines, hold your pencil at the top and press very lightly, moving the pencil at a steady speed. Feint lines are used as **construction lines** – lines which are not part of the finished drawing.

To draw dark lines in any direction, hold your pencil near the point and press harder. Rotate your pencil slightly as you draw the line. Dark lines are used as **outlines** – lines which show the shape of the object.

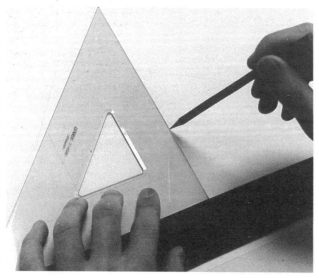

When drawing vertical lines, use the fingers of your other hand to hold the set square against the T-square.

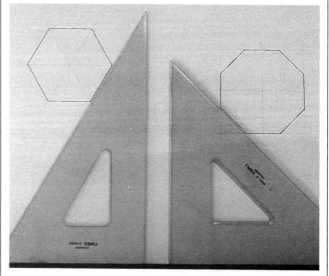

To draw lines at various angles, the set squares can be turned over, and any edge held against the T-square.

Measuring

Measure along a feint line you have already drawn. Your eyes must be directly over the point you are marking. Mark each end of the measurement with a dot.

In CDT we use millimetres or metres (not centimetres) as the main unit of measurements.

Compasses

Never guess the centre of a circle. As the centre is a point, two feint lines which cross are needed to show it.

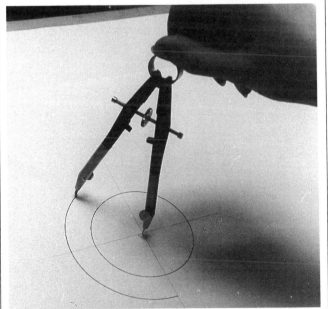

Set the radius carefully against a ruler. Hold the compasses at the top and guide the point to the centre with your other hand.

Lean the compasses slightly in the direction of rotation and twist them between two fingers as shown.

Scale

The **scale** of a drawing shows how much smaller or bigger than the real object the drawing is. Your drawings should usually be to one of these standard scales:

Full size	1:1		
Reduced	1:2	1:5	1:10
	1:20	1:50	1:100
	1:200	1:500	1:1000
Enlarged	2:1	5:1	10:1
	20:1	50:1	100:1
	200:1	500:1	1000:1

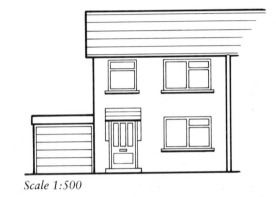

Scale 1:500

The house is drawn to a scale of 1:500. The pen nib is drawn five times its actual size (scale 5:1).

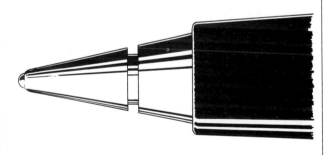

Scale 5:1

ACTIVITIES

Use A4 cartridge paper for each of these activities.

1 Start at any point on the edge of the sheet. Draw feint lines using the 45° set square, so they 'bounce' off the edges as shown.

Draw dark lines over some of the rectangles, so they stand out clearly.

This is called **lining in**. Each rectangle is an **outline**.

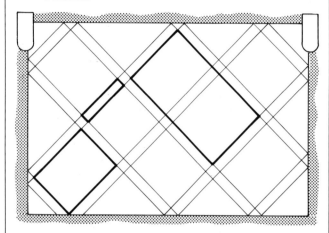

2 Measure half way along each edge of your paper. Draw feint vertical and horizontal construction lines, and diagonal lines at 45° as shown.

Draw the smallest square, which was 10mm sides, in the centre. Continue drawing the pattern of squares until you run out of space. These squares should be outlines.

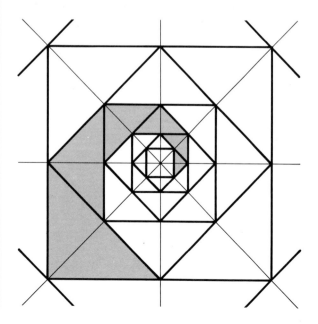

Lay a sheet of bank paper over this pattern. Try to create a pleasing colour scheme using colouring pencils. The drawing shows the start of a spiral design as an example.

Carefully colour your original drawing in your chosen colour scheme.

3 Produce an accurate drawing of this Mitsubishi logo, which is based on an equilateral triangle. Make the sides of the triangle 90mm.

Do not line in the outline before you have drawn all the construction lines.

Colour the logo in one colour only using a felt tip pen.

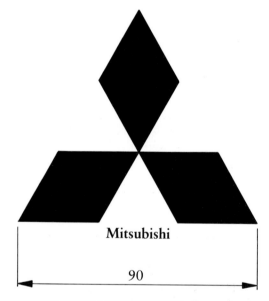

Mitsubishi

90

ACTIVITIES

4 The drawing shows several types of truss, a framework used for building bridges.

Trusses are always based on triangles. Do you know why?

If the full size height of each truss is 2 metres, draw each one to a scale of 1:50.

Draw the top and bottom construction lines for each truss first. Space them one above the other on your paper.

Measure the span of each truss and calculate the full size spans. Print under each truss its name, full size height and span. Print a suitable title and the scale at the bottom of your drawing.

Examples of trusses

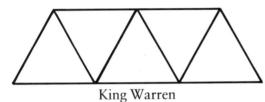

King Warren

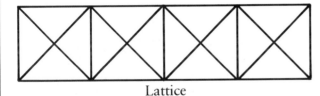

Lattice

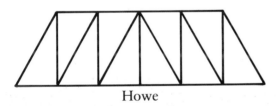

Howe

5 Divide the top and side edges of your paper into four and draw centre lines as shown.

Draw a 80mm diameter circle on each centre.

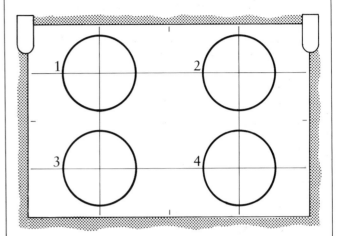

Each circle represents a cake which has to be cut into slices. Using only your T-square, set squares and pencil, divide each cake like this:

Cake   1 – 6 equal slices (use 60°/30° set square)
Cake   2 – 8 equal slices (use 45° set square)
Cake   3 – 12 equal slices (use 60°/30° set square)
Cake   4 – 24 equal slices (use both set squares)

Line in the edges of the slices so they are clearly shown.

Clip or tape a sheet of bank paper over the finished cake drawing. By joining points on the circles, try to create various shapes:

● stars with 6, 8, 12 and 24 points
● polygons
● any others you can discover for yourself.

Line in these shapes with a ballpoint pen, or colour them.

ACTIVITIES

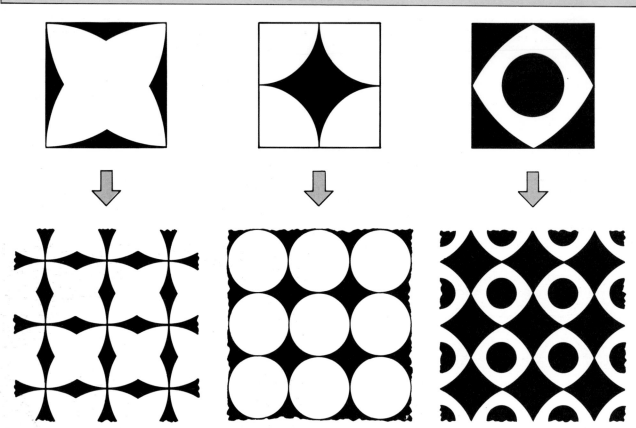

The patterns formed by tesselating the tiles shown

6 Tiles are attractive because they tesselate (repeat without leaving gaps) to create interesting patterns.

Prepare a 1:2 scale drawing showing these existing designs, and the outlines for three new ones, as shown opposite. All the tiles are 150mm square.

Clip or tape a sheet of bank paper over your drawing. Use this to experiment with your instruments to create new tile designs.

For each new design, trace, freehand, several tiles together on another sheet of bank paper. Colour the tiles to see the pattern this creates, using no more than two colours.

Repeat this until you have three new tile designs which create attractive patterns.

Draw and colour your final three designs on the original drawing.

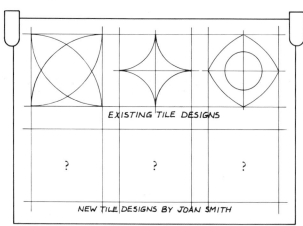

EXISTING TILE DESIGNS

? ? ?

NEW TILE DESIGNS BY JOAN SMITH

Drawing layout

ACTIVITIES

7 The drawing shows the arrangement of ten red snooker balls, each 40mm diameter, at the start of a game.

Using a scale of 1:2, draw the construction lines as shown, then the circles, followed by the triangle.

A design for the snooker triangle (used to set up the balls) uses three identical pieces of wood 16mm thick. Draw the triangle around the balls.

Colour the balls using a red felt marker. Leave a 'highlight' at the same position on each ball, as shown in the example below. Add wood grain to the triangle.

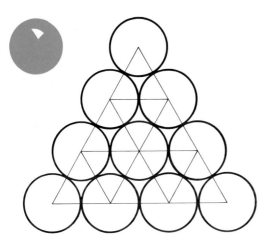

Dennis Taylor

8 The photograph below shows the playing card symbols, and a method of drawing the outline of a Spade.

Draw four sets of centre lines, and construct the Spade symbol, 50mm wide, using one of the centre lines.

By experiment, design suitable outlines for the other three symbols, each 50mm wide, using drawing instruments.

Carefully colour the symbols using felt markers.

Playing card symbols

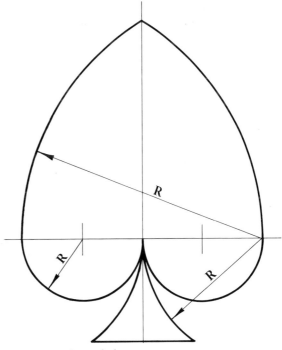

Drawing a Spade symbol

33

Working drawings

These are drawings which contain all the information needed to make the product, such as:

- the exact dimensions of each part
- the way the parts fit together
- the material each part is made from
- how each part is finished (e.g. paint, varnish, plastic coating).

Orthographic projection is usually used for working drawings, although pictorial views may be used as well. Some information, such as the material and finish, is best communicated by means of notes.

Working drawings must give information which is **correct** and **exact**. It is very expensive if, for example, ten thousand wrongly made brackets have to be scrapped because the drawing was not clear!

Certain rules must be followed if working drawings are to be understood by other people. Some of these you know already, such as the rules of orthographic projection. Other important rules are shown below.

Types of lines

——————————————— construction lines (thin, feint)

———————————————— outlines (thick, dark)

——————————————— dimension lines and hatching (thin)

— — — — — — — — — hidden lines (thin dashes)

——— - ——— - ——— centre lines (thin 'chain' line)

Dimensioning

A well-dimensioned drawing should be clear and easy to understand.

- Dimension lines should be well clear of the outline, and spaced well apart.
- Arrowheads should be thin, like spear points, and filled in.
- Print the actual dimensions clearly, and not too small.
- Dimensions should be read from the bottom or the right of the drawing.
- Ø is a symbol meaning 'diameter'.
- R means 'radius'.

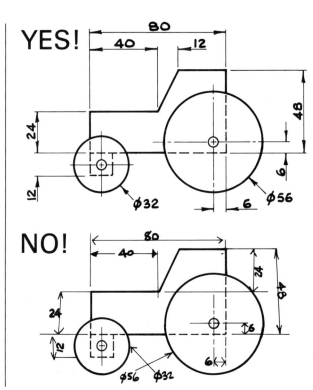

Correct and incorrect ways of dimensioning

Sections

Drawing a section is a way of showing the inside of an object. Imagine the object is sliced in half, throw away the part nearest to you, and look at what is left.

In working drawings, sectioned parts are shown by **hatching**. This means drawing thin lines at 45° where each part has been sliced, as in the example shown here.

In illustrations, the sectioned area can be shown a different colour to make it stand out. Pictorial views can also be sectioned.

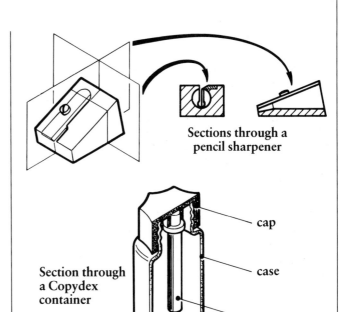

Sections through a pencil sharpener

Section through a Copydex container

- cap
- case
- brush

Printing

The title, scale, notes and other written information need to be printed carefully on working drawings. Always draw feint guidelines first.

Think of printing as **drawings** of letters and numbers rather than as writing. Draw each line of a character as a separate stroke – raise your pencil between strokes. For example, print an 8 as two circles.

Practise printing your name, address and telephone number in the different heights and styles shown.

You can use stencils for large letters in titles or headings. They give neat results but are rather slow to use.

PRINT USING GUIDE LINES
LIKE THIS
5mm HIGH FOR TITLES
3mm HIGH OR 4mm HIGH
FOR NOTES AND ITEM LISTS
lower case lettering is suitable for
notes. More guide lines are needed
– these are 2mm apart
1 2 3 4 5 6 7 8 9 0
A B C D E F G H I J K L M N
O P Q R S T U V W X Y Z

Using templates

Templates are available of shapes which sometimes need to be repeatedly drawn, such as nuts or electronics symbols. They are quick to use and give very neat results. You can use them with a pencil or ballpoint pen.

The most useful templates are those for drawing circles and ellipses. Draw the centre lines first, and line these up carefully with the centre lines on the template. Hold your pencil or pen upright when drawing the shape.

French curves are used to draw complex curves accurately.

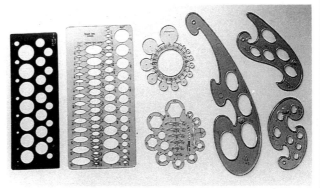

A selection of templates

Producing working drawings

1 Sketch final design

This is the starting point for any working drawing. It should show the most important information needed, with notes where necessary. It is best drawn to scale using isometric or square grid paper.

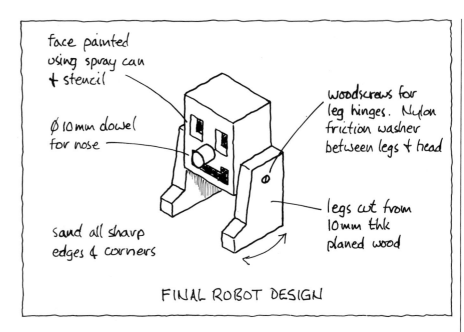

2 Sketch layout

Now concentrate on designing the drawing itself. Think carefully what needs to be shown. Draw an outline sketch of where you think each part of the drawing will fit. Work out the scale of the drawing, to make the views and notes fit the size of paper you are using.

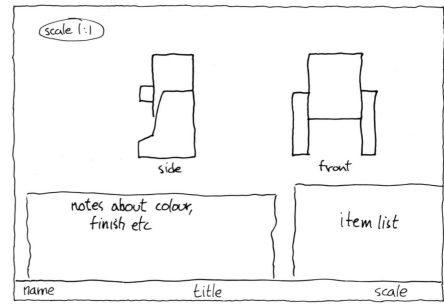

3 Construct layout

Have your design sketch and layout sketch beside you to work from. Draw the most important construction lines for each view. You can measure directly from your design sketch if it is drawn to the same scale, and you have used a grid.

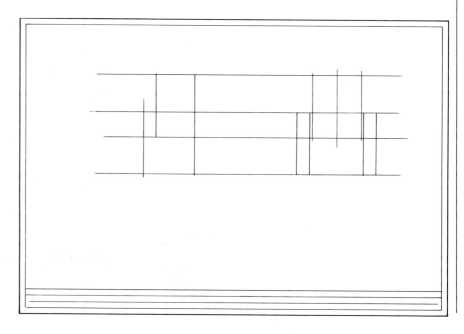

4 Construct outlines

Measure and draw the other lines for each view. Add other details such as the item list and title block. Allow plenty of space around each view for dimensioning. You should still use feint construction lines at this stage. Any mistakes can then easily be corrected.

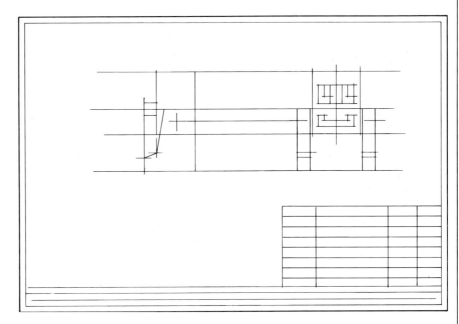

5 Line in outlines

Line in the outlines of all the views. Work in this order: circles, horizontal lines, vertical lines, other lines. Hidden lines can be shown if this helps to make the drawing clear. Sometimes they can be confusing and should be left out.

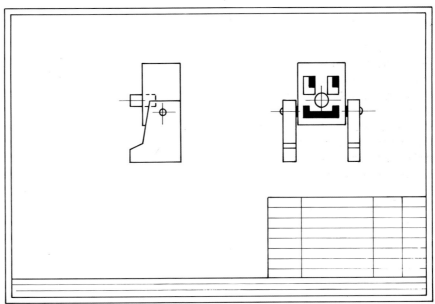

6 Add details

Think carefully which dimensions are needed to make all the parts. Draw the dimension lines and arrowheads, and print the dimensions. Write the item list and notes on a piece of rough paper before printing them on your drawing. Use 'balloons' to label each part with its item number.

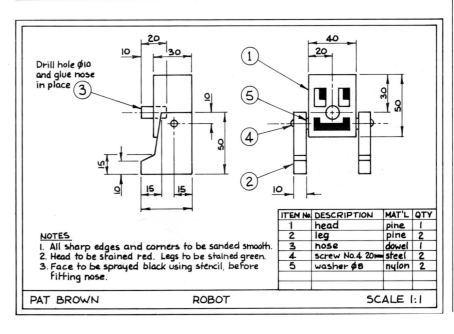

Drill hole Ø10 and glue nose in place ③

NOTES
1. All sharp edges and corners to be sanded smooth.
2. Head to be stained red. Legs to be stained green.
3. Face to be sprayed black using stencil, before fitting nose.

ITEM No	DESCRIPTION	MAT'L	QTY
1	head	pine	1
2	leg	pine	2
3	nose	dowel	1
4	screw No.4 20mm	steel	2
5	washer Ø8	nylon	2

PAT BROWN   ROBOT   SCALE 1:1

ACTIVITIES

Use A4 cartridge paper for each of these drawings.

1 The photograph shows a block and ball puzzle. The aim is to arrange the balls so they are next to each other.

From the design sketch shown, prepare a full size (scale 1:1) drawing of the block. Work out the dimensions from the grid.

Two views will be needed to show both holes.

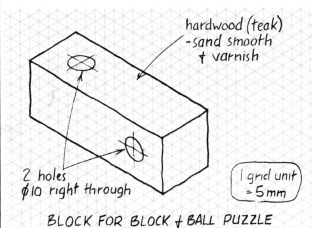

hardwood (teak)
-sand smooth
+ varnish

2 holes
⌀10 right through

1 grid unit
= 5mm

BLOCK FOR BLOCK & BALL PUZZLE

2 This is a final design sketch for a coat hook. It is to be formed by bending aluminium alloy strip to the shape shown.

The end is radiused to prevent coat collars being torn by sharp corners. 'Csk' stands for countersunk – this is the type of screw which fixes the coat hook to the wall or batten.

Produce a full size working drawing of the coat hook.

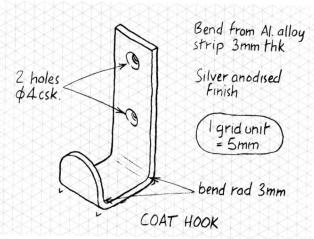

Bend from Al. alloy
strip 3mm thk

Silver anodised
finish

1 grid unit
= 5mm

2 holes
⌀4 csk.

bend rad 3mm

COAT HOOK

3 This yo-yo body consists of two moulded plastic sides which are connected by a spindle made from wooden dowel.

No adhesive is used. The holes are slightly smaller than the dowel diameter, and the parts are pressed firmly together.

Produce a full size working drawing of the complete yo-yo, choosing suitable dimensions.

Show how you would attach the string to the spindle. Design a suitable label and show this on your working drawing.

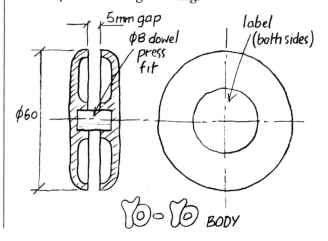

5mm gap
⌀8 dowel
press fit

label
(both sides)

⌀60

YO-YO BODY

ACTIVITIES

4 The sketch shows a design for a three dimensional noughts and crosses game. Coloured pegs are inserted in the holes.

The board is made from clear acrylic plastic. This is a thermoplastic material which can be shaped by heating it to a suitable temperature.

Produce a full size working drawing of the board. Design a suitable peg and include this on your drawing.

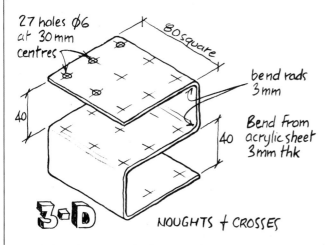

5 The photograph shows a fruitbowl made from teak by turning on a lathe.

Design a wooden fruitbowl of your own and produce a working drawing of it. Start by sketching sections of shapes for the bowl. Decide what qualities you are aiming for.

You will probably need French curves to produce an accurate side elevation and section. Show the overall dimensions only.

6 This sketch shows an idea for a model hovercraft. It is made from stiff card and expanded polystyrene cut from a ceiling tile, and glued together using fabric adhesive.

Sketch ideas for a similar hovercraft and produce a working drawing of your final design.

You could also make the model from your drawing and evaluate its performance (see Chapter 5 on making models).

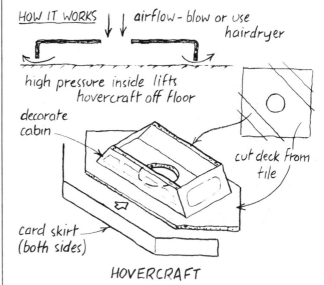

Model hovercraft made from a ceiling tile and card

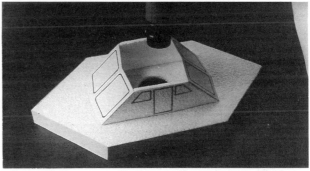

7 Design a wooden tray or rack to hold these drawing instruments: set squares, ruler, compasses, pencil and rubber.

Arrange the instruments in different ways and sketch these different layouts. Try to leave as little unused space as possible.

Sketch ideas for making your tray or rack using plywood, dowel and softwood strips.

Produce a working drawing of your final design.

Illustrations

The purpose of an illustration is to show a particular aspect of an article as clearly as possible, for example, its appearance, how to use it, how it works or how to repair it.

The illustrations below are all taken from various leaflets or brochures. Can you work out what each illustration is trying to show?

Headings and other words are often necessary in illustrations, where these communicate better than pictures. Illustrations can be drawn using the actual object, or a working drawing as a guide. They can also be traced from photographs or computer print-outs, and altered as necessary.

A selection of illustrations from leaflets and brochures

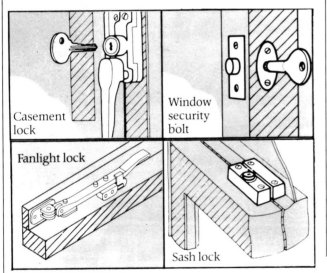

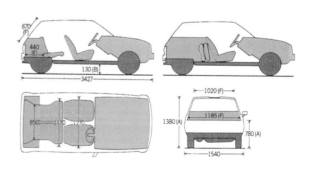

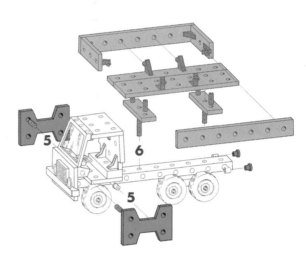

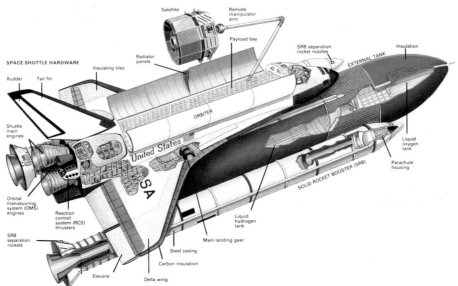

Producing illustrations

Illustrations need to be designed, just like objects. So write a specification, answering such questions as:

- What information must the illustration show?
- What size should it be?
- Where will it be used?

Sketch ideas for various layouts, including any necessary or useful words. Select the best layout, using your specification as a guide. The sketches below show the selected final layouts for each illustration.

Use the method of working suggested for working drawings (see pages 36–37). Draw the main features in feint pencil lines first. Use colour, shading and printing as necessary to finish the drawing. Use instruments where possible.

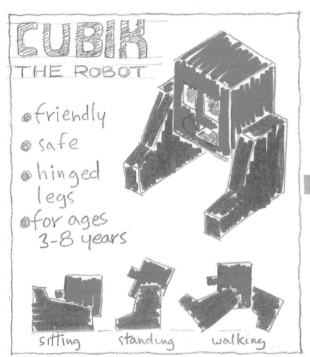

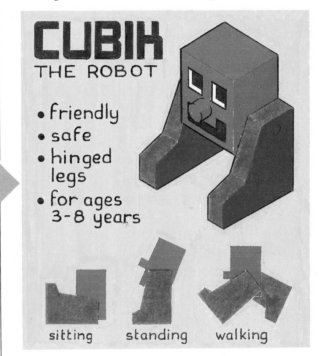

The final stages in designing an advertisement for the robot. Advertisements should attract attention to a product's desirable features

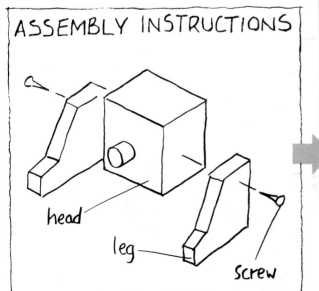

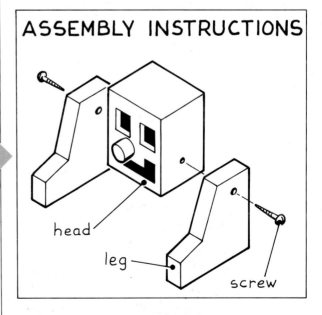

A design sketch and final leaflet showing how to fit the parts of the robot together. An outline 'exploded' view is appropriate for this

ACTIVITIES

1 Start a collection of illustrations and mount them on dark coloured card to display, as in the photograph below.

There are several ways to arrange such a collection. Here are four suggestions:

Illustrations used in advertisements – from the back pages of newspapers, sales catalogues (e.g. Argos), magazines, leaflets, labels on cartons.

Illustrations giving instructions – from handbooks and manuals (e.g. how to assemble a plastic model kit, how to adjust or repair a domestic appliance or vehicle).

Illustrations giving information – from magazines, books and occasional advertisements (e.g. cutaway drawings of buildings, aircraft, machines, often naming various parts).

Illustrations about a particular kind of product – e.g. board games, computers, book covers. You can make a useful collection as part of your research for a design project.

Here are some questions to discuss about your collection:

- Why are photographs often used in advertisements?
- Why are illustrations in newspapers usually black and white?
- What is a **ghosted** drawing?
- What is an **exploded** view?
- Why are colours sometimes used which are not the actual colour of the object?

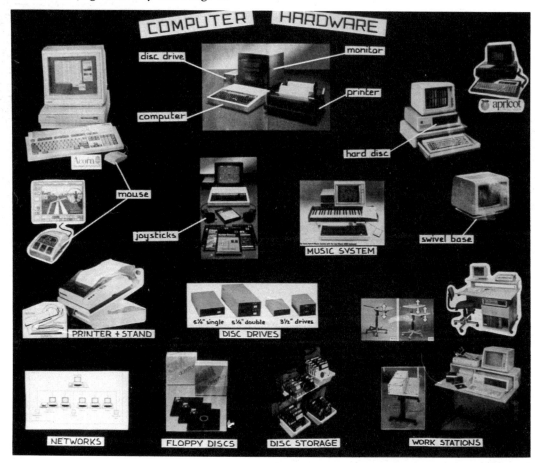

A collection of illustrations displayed

2 Try producing 'cut and paste' illustrations. Create a new illustration by cutting out and mounting an existing one on a new background. New details can be added as required.

Find an advertisement illustration for an object which interests you. Use this to make an informative illustration by naming the main parts. Add a title and any other information you think would be useful.

ACTIVITIES

3 Obtain a simple puzzle or child's toy, or see the photograph and sketch of the block and ball puzzle on page 38.

Decide suitable dimensions for a box to house the puzzle. Draw, twice full size, a label advertising the puzzle, to be glued to the box lid.

The advertisement should mention the main features of the puzzle or toy, and be bright and attractive.

4 Decorative candles can be made at home using a candle making kit. The kit consists of special moulds, flaked wax, string, dye and a booklet describing how to make candles.

An illustration is needed to show some of the shapes and colours of candles that may be made using such a kit.

Produce an illustration as part of the instruction booklet, showing at least six different candles. Colour and shade your drawings carefully.

5 Obtain a simple object that you can take apart, such as a small torch, a ballpoint pen, a clothes peg or a small construction toy.

Examine the object carefully, and measure the main dimensions of the parts. Draw *either* a section *or* an exploded view, showing how the parts fit together. Name the parts, and add a title to your illustration.

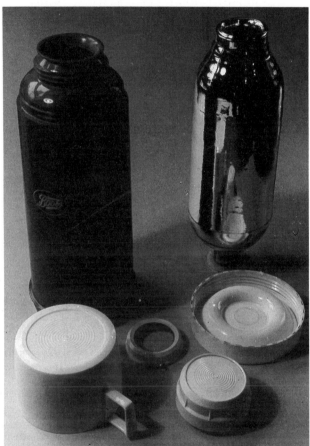

5 | Models and mock-ups

Why models?

For some people, making model railways or aircraft is a favourite hobby. Designers, however, use models to **explore, test** or **demonstrate** possible solutions to design problems, before making the final product.

To be useful, a model must be quicker, easier or cheaper to make than the final product. A model is made for a definite purpose, and should be designed and made with that end in mind.

To explore how a solution will look

No drawing can be completely realistic. A model can be seen from any viewpoint. Appearance can be very important, for example in buildings, ornaments or furniture.

A model can also be made to any scale. Small-scale architectural models like this one can help planners and the public to evaluate the design before building starts.

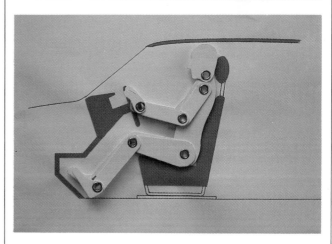

To test whether a solution will work

Many things that are designed and made need to be easy to hold, turn, reach or sit in. Finding out about making things easy to use is called **ergonomics.**

This jointed card model of a human figure is being used on a scale drawing of a driving seat and car controls. Details of how to make this model are given on page 95 of this book.

To demonstrate how a solution works

This petrol engine has been cut away to reveal the moving parts. It can be turned by hand so that the working of the mechanism can be clearly seen at each stage.

Where parts have been cut away, they have been painted to make this clear. The spark plug has been replaced by a bulb which lights at the correct position of the piston.

Materials

Almost anything can be used for model making, but many models can be made with only a few materials and tools.

The information below is a guide to help you get started. You should also experiment for yourself.

Part or shape	Material	Part or shape	Material
Flat surface	stiff card, corrugated card, balsa wood sheet, plastic sheet, ceiling tiles, thin plywood.	Complex shapes with double curvature	Air drying clay, plasticine, cellulose filler (e.g. Polyfilla)
Box shapes (prisms and pyramids)	large: development on card or paper, expanded polystyrene small: balsa wood, cork (e.g. from wine bottle corks)	Hinges, flexible joins	folded paper or card, masking tape, dyelets, split fasteners, flexible plastic sheet, string, rubber bands
Round shapes (cylinders or cones)	large: development on card or paper, scrap card tubes or cartons small: wood dowel, drinking straws, wire	Mechanical parts or complete machanisms	card, balsa wood, wood dowel, wire, plastic sheet, eyelets, rubber bands, construction kits (Technical Lego, Fischer Technik, Meccano)

Glue	Material	Glue	Material
Fabric glue (e.g. Copydex) or PVA	paper, card ,expanded polystyrene, cork, fabric	Masking tape, Sellotape	almost anything (but weak)
Balsa cement	balsa wood, cellulose acetate sheet	Staples or eyelets	not a glue, but quick and easy for fixing paper, card, soft plastic sheets
Polystyrene cement	polystyrene plastic sheet		

Colouring

Felt markers, colouring pencils, poster colour and ink can be used on paper and card. Plastics can be sprayed with car touch-up paint. Using coloured paper or card, collected from discarded packaging, can make colouring unnecessary.

Tools

Drawing instruments
Scissors
Craft knife and steel straight edge
Cutting board (thick sheet of card)
Sandpaper
Eyelet pliers

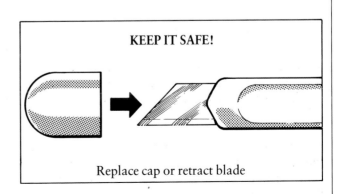

KEEP IT SAFE!

Replace cap or retract blade

Developments

Unfolding or unrolling the surfaces of a shape gives you its development.
Open up a rectangular box:

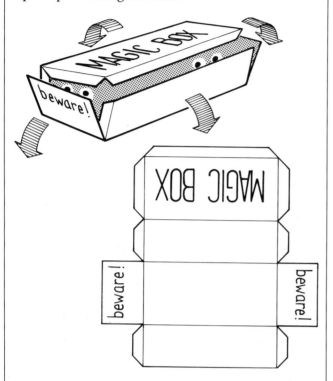

Developments should be drawn with instruments on thick paper or card. You need to find the **true lengths** of all the edges of the solid, usually from orthographic views. Many shapes can be made from variations of the ones shown here, or several glued together. These examples are shown without glue tabs.

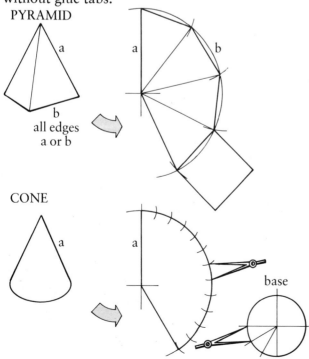

PYRAMID

all edges
a or b

CONE

base

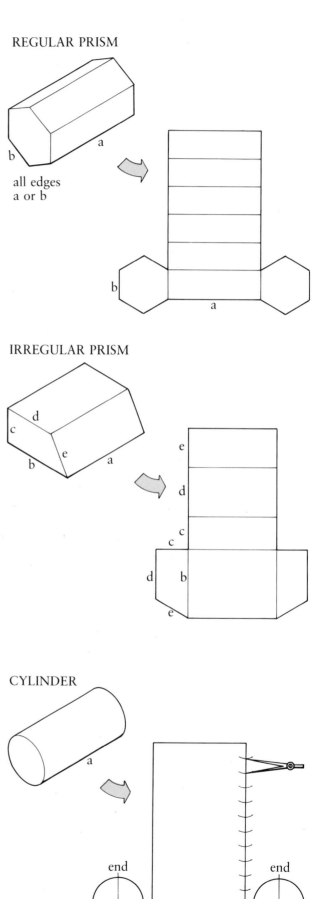

REGULAR PRISM

all edges
a or b

IRREGULAR PRISM

CYLINDER

end   end

ACTIVITY

These drawings show some models based on the geometrical solids shown on the previous page. The models can be made by joining several simple solids. You can also use things like straws or table tennis balls as part of a model.

For each of the drawings shown, name which geometrical solids they are made from.

Think of a similar object which interests you, yet would be difficult to make full size or fully functioning. Design and make a model of it from your imagination, using these two pages as a guide.

Start by sketching pictorial views of several ideas. Draw the development of each solid on thin card. Add glue tabs as necessary, and cut out the outline.

Bend the fold lines carefully against a ruler. Check that your development is correct by folding it loosely together, then glue the tabs. Rubber bands or masking tape are useful for holding the model together until the glue has set.

As the purpose is to explore the appearance of the real object, you should make your model look as realistic as possible. Apart from painting, any colouring or drawing should be done before assembling the model.

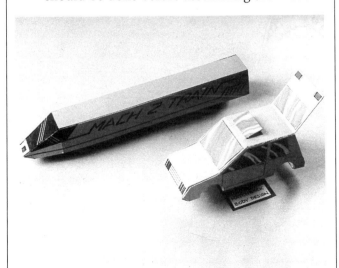

Some finished models

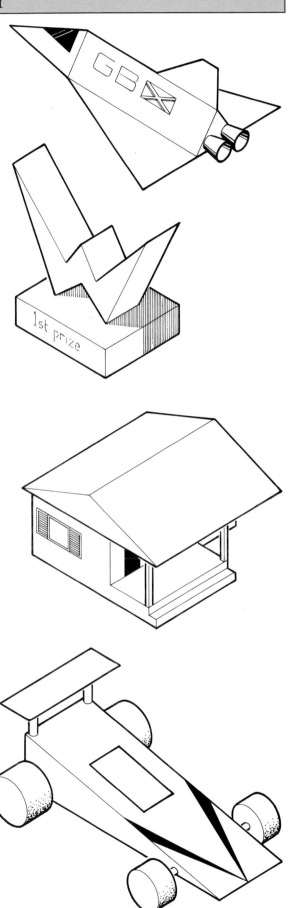

Packaging

Almost everything we buy is packaged. Manufacturers spend a great deal of time and money designing packages, sometimes more than on the products themselves. Can you think why they do this?

Packages take many forms – cartons, bags, bottles, tubes, sacks, cans. The package designer has to think about the most important things that any particular package has to do.

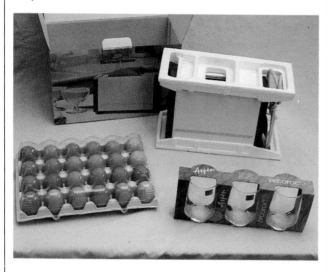

Fragile things need to be protected from shock. One method is to surround the item with flexible padding inside a hard shell. Egg cartons are strengthened by the eggs themselves – an egg is strong if pressed only on the ends.

Display packaging is designed mainly to make people want to buy the product. Sometimes they are badly designed in other ways – some are bulky to store and difficult to reseal once opened.

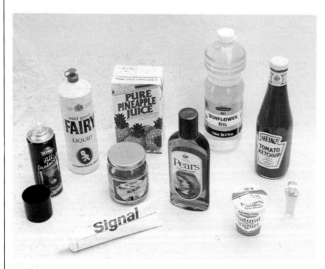

Liquids are usually packaged in plastic or plastic lined cartons. The liquids can be squeezed, poured, sprayed or scooped out with a spoon, according to their use. For some reason, people prefer tomato ketchup in bottles, which is wasteful, rather than in tubes.

Enormous waste is created by discarded packaging. Each year 19 million tonnes of household rubbish is buried in refuse tips like this one. Packages which rot quickly cause less pollution than plastic, metal foil and aluminium cans.

ACTIVITIES

1 Copy the table below. Think how each package is used. Tick the qualities you think are important for each type of package.

Collect packages which contain these items. Display and investigate them. Do they have all the qualities you considered important? Draw another table and record your investigation. Discuss your findings.

Specification check list	Bleach	Cassette player	Crisps	Child's game	Breakfast cereal	Coffee powder	Tissues	Sausage rolls	Light bulb	Flower seeds
Strength										
Eyecatching appearance										
States contents										
Displays contents										
Easy to open										
Difficult to open										
Easy to reseal										
Easy to stack										
Protects contents from:										
• shock										
• moisture										
• bacteria										
Cheap to make										
Shows danger warning										
Shows instructions for use										
Does not cause pollution										

2 Unfold some of the packages you collected for Activity 1 and lay them flat. These are developments like those on the previous two pages.

Choose one of the developments and draw around it on thin card. Cut out the shape and fold it along the same lines as the original package.

Think of a suitable alternative product to go in the package. Design suitable illustrations and text for the outside.

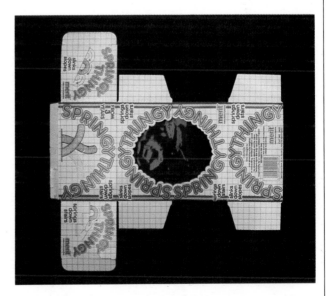

3 Below are ideas for packages for you to design and make. Start by listing a specification and producing sketches of ideas.

- A package to hold and display a pair of set squares (45° and 60°/30°).

- A package to contain six sticks of blackboard chalk. The chalk must not break when the pack is dropped on to a hard floor from a height of one metre.

- A pack for a new kind of sweet called Juciballs. Juciballs are spherical, about 10mm diameter and made in various colours. The manufacturers would like an attractive pack which dispenses the sweets one at a time, and can be resealed.

Compare and discuss your finished designs.

Mechanisms

Mechanisms are to do with making things move in the way we want them to move. We want an egg whisk to have beaters which turn very quickly. A mechanical saw needs a blade which moves back and forth quite slowly.

This section deals with simple 2-D hand-powered mechanisms which can be made in the graphics room. This is a effective way of making demonstration models of large machines, and of testing your own ideas.

Mechanisms – for changing the direction and speed of motion

These drawings of mechanisms are for you to refer to when designing your own models.

It is a good idea to make simple models of these using a construction kit such as Technical Lego or

Fischer Technik. You will then find it easier to design and make your own models using other materials.

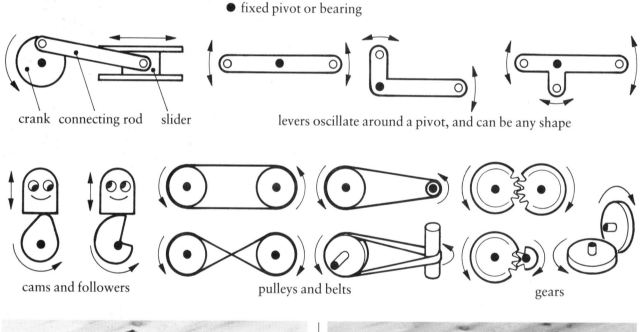

● fixed pivot or bearing

crank connecting rod slider

levers oscillate around a pivot, and can be any shape

cams and followers

pulleys and belts

gears

Mechanisms made from a technical construction kit

Designing and making moving picture models

These card models are made to work by turning a handle (crank) on the back or front. Part of the mechanism can be hidden on the back if necessary.

The models can demonstrate an existing mechanism, or be based on an idea from your imagination, like the arguing men below.

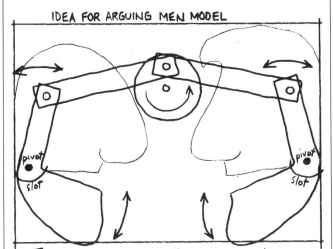

Turning crank moves both jaws up and down

You need two pieces of thick card about 150mm × 100mm. One piece will be the picture background, and the moving parts cut from the other piece. You also need scissors, a craft knife, eyelets, eyelet pliers and a suitable hole punch.

Sketch a suitable mechanism using a crank, levers and connecting rods. Part of the levers are the men's jaws in this example. Shape the other ends of the levers so that they can be operated by the connecting rods.

Draw the outlines of all the moving parts, using a ruler where possible. Make all the moving parts at least 10mm wide, or they will be too weak.

Trace all the moving parts on to one of your pieces of card. Cut them out and punch holes for the pivots and pins. If necessary, mark and cut suitable slots in the background card for the levers to pass through.

The model can now be assembled, using eyelets and the eyelet pliers. The eyelets should be loose so that the parts can move freely.

Test your model by turning the crank. If it sticks, examine it carefully. The most likely faults are:

- the connecting rods are too long or too short
- the eyelets are too tight
- the slots (if used) are not long enough to allow for the full lever movement.

Draw and colour your picture. Glue a small piece of dowel in the crankpin eyelet to use as a handle.

Front

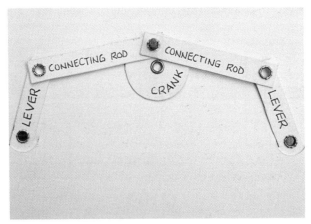

Back

Eyelets, eyelet pliers and hole punch

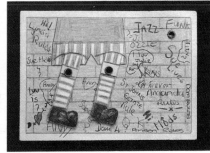

Examples of completed models

ACTIVITIES

1 Make this demonstration model which shows how the main moving parts of a four-stroke petrol engine work.

Look at the working drawing below. You need two pieces of stiff card 150mm × 100mm, and tools as described on page 51. One of the card pieces is the backplate to which the engine parts are fitted.

- Draw guidelines accurately on the backplate as shown. Punch the hole for the crankshaft.

- Draw and cut out the other parts carefully, and punch holes as necessary.

- Glue the spacer and 'cylinder' strips to the backplate.

- Fit the piston, connecting rod and crank together with two eyelets. Do not press the eyelet pliers too hard – the joints need to be loose.

- Slide the piston into the cylinder. Fix the crankshaft to the backplate with another eyelet.

- Using epoxy resin, glue a short piece of dowel to the crankpin to serve as a handle.

- By drawing and colouring make your model as realistic as possible.

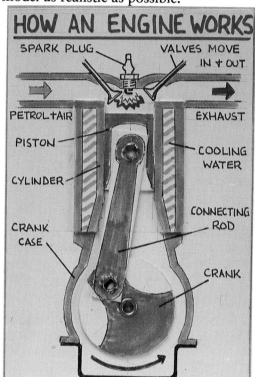

HOW AN ENGINE WORKS

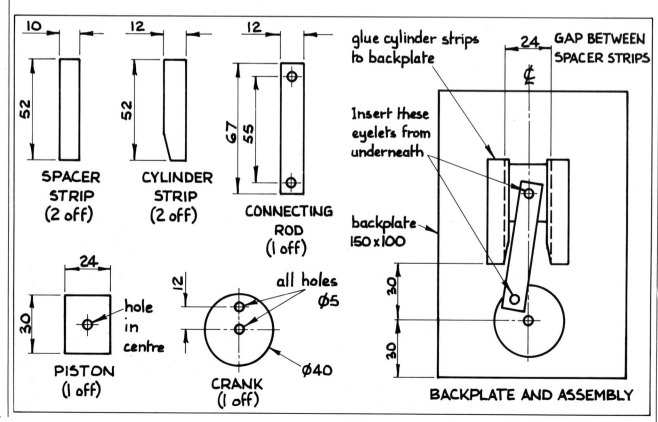

ACTIVITIES

2 The sketch and notes below describe the mechanism for a child's pedal car.

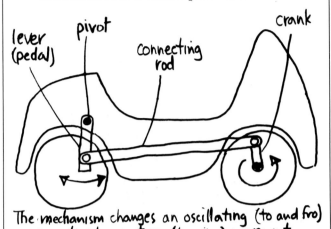

The mechanism changes an oscillating (to and fro) movement into a rotary (turning) movement

Find examples of some of the objects below. Sketch their basic mechanisms, and make notes on how they work.

Design and make a working demonstration model of one or more of them.

folding umbrella
cork puller (for wine bottles)
kitchen scales
playground rocking horse
mechanical workshop saw
automatic door closing mechanism
bicycle brakes
bicycle pump
parallel motion drawing board
squeege floor mop
mechanical excavator

3 Sketch your own ideas for a picture, part of which moves. Some examples are shown below.

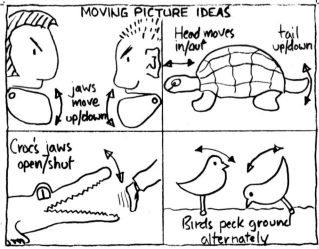

Sketches of ideas for moving pictures

- Make your idea interesting or amusing.
- Make the moving parts large.
- The movements must repeat.
- Show the movements clearly by means of arrows.

Design and make a moving picture model of your favourite idea. Use the information on page 51 to help you.

4 W. Heath Robinson was an artist who drew cartoon pictures of imaginary machines.

The machines often perform useless or amusing tasks, and look almost, but not quite, impossible to work. Can you see how the one in the picture is supposed to work?

Describe and sketch ideas for 'Heath Robinson' machines which could:

- Wake you up in the morning by hitting you on the head.
- Mix a milkshake automatically when you pull a lever.
- Feed the cat whilst you are away on holiday.

Pop-up books

These clever and fascinating books are examples of **paper engineering**. All kinds of movements can be made to happen by folding, bending and sliding shapes made from thin card.

You can learn a lot by investigating pop-up books like these. Look carefully at the way different effects are achieved. They are often surprisingly simple.

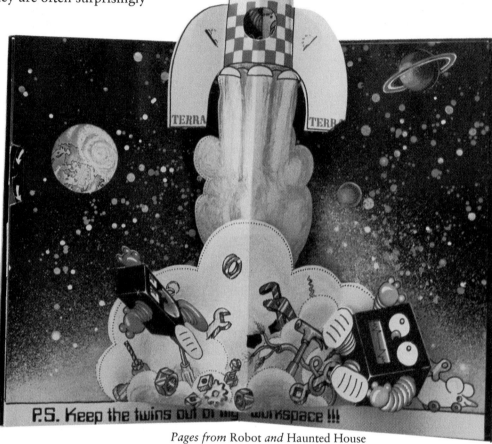

Pages from Robot *and* Haunted House

To experiment making pop-up models, you need a pencil and ruler, thin card, scissors and paper glue. It also helps to have a vivid imagination.

Test your basic idea by making a simple model. It is quite likely that this first model will not work properly.

Look at it carefully, and try to see what you need to change to improve it. Alter it or make a second model and test this version.

Once you have found how to achieve the movement that you want, you can make a final model to the same pattern. This can be drawn on and coloured as necessary.

ACTIVITY

These drawings show some of the techniques used in making pop-up models. Try to find out about other techniques as well.

Here are some ideas for pop-up models for you to design and make:

- A birthday card to a friend. A cartoon animal opens its mouth to say 'Happy Birthday'.
- A ghost which appears when you open a door.
- A bird which flaps its wings.
- A farmyard scene. Buildings and animals stand up when you open the model.

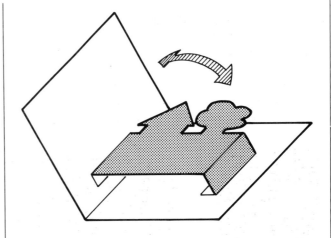

Parallelogram movement

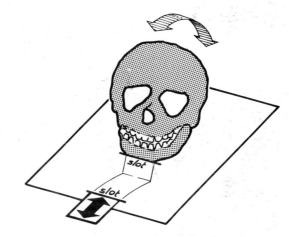

Lever movement

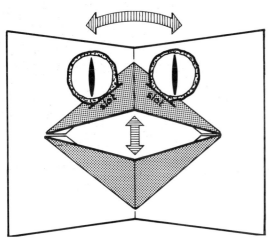

Triangles fold open and closed

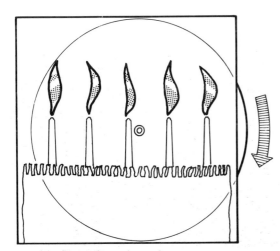

Rotating disc shows through windows

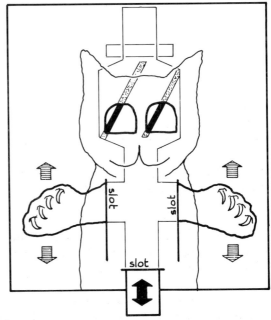

Sliding movement

6 | Signs, symbols and logos

These are all ways of communicating by means of pictures or shapes.

Symbols

A symbol is a simple drawing or shape which represents a thing or an idea. People have been using symbols for at least ten thousand years. Our written language is made up of symbols – the letters of the alphabet, numerals and punctuation marks.

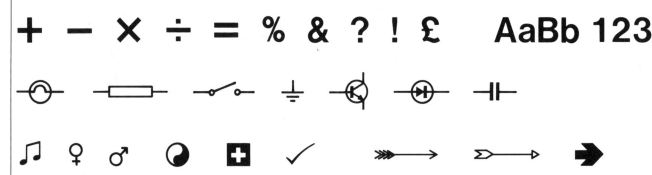

Above are examples of **abstract** symbols. We have to learn what they mean before we can use them.

Many abstract symbols started as pictures. The arrow was once a picture of an arrow shot from a bow. Over centuries the shape changed, but the meaning remains the same.

These are examples of **pictorial** symbols. They are simple pictures which can be easily understood.

A symbol can be used as part of a sign (see next page). Symbols are also used, for example, on vehicle dashboards and on maps or charts. Computer symbols called **icons** are often used in computer aided design (see Chapter 10).

56

Signs

A sign displays **information**, an **instruction** or a **warning**. You see them almost everywhere – in shops, streets, schools, libraries, garages and workplaces. Signs are often a combination of several symbols.

Road signs are familiar examples. The main types are shown below. Notice how the colours convey meaning as well as the shape. A complete set of road signs is published in the Highway Code, and in many road atlases.

INFORMATION Usually rectangular with blue background	DO . . . Usually circular with blue background	DO NOT . . . Usually circular with red border	WARNING Usually triangular with red border
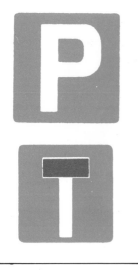	 	 	 

Safety signs

The signs opposite are recommended by the British Standards Institution for use in workplaces and schools. Why is it especially important that their meanings should be clear?

WARNING	DO NOT . . .	DO . . .

Signs and symbols in everyday life

Designing signs and symbols

A sign or symbol should communicate a simple message clearly and quickly. Here are some points to bear in mind when designing your own.

- *Choose a familiar viewpoint.* Look at the symbols on page 56. The side view of the bus is easy to recognise. A plan view would simply be a rectangle, and a front view could just as well be a lorry.

- *Keep the design very simple.* The bus symbol consists of a few rectangles and circles, yet it could only be a bus. Include only the main features of the object you are using as a symbol.

- *Use large, bold shapes.* Thin lines and tiny details are no use at all in signs and symbols. Draw bold, geometrical shapes, using drawing instruments where possible.

- *Use colour for meaning and contrast.* Red is understood to mean danger, so using red in warning signs adds impact to the message. Bright colours stand out clearly on a wall or in the street, and help to attract attention.

Designing a restaurant sign

Brief: Design a sign to hang in a department store which means 'this way to the restaurant'.

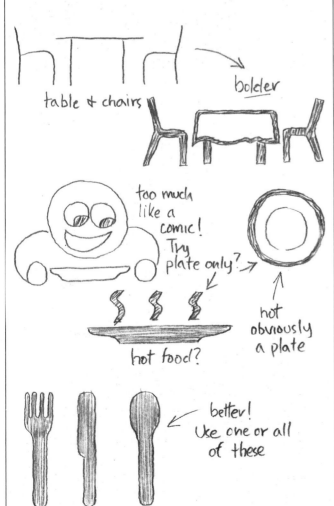

We need to think of possible symbols for a restaurant. Write down some ideas:
eating, drinking, food, table, chairs, plate, knife, fork and spoon.

Now select the most promising ideas and draw simple sketches of them.

The simplest and clearest symbols seem to be the knife, fork and spoon. Only two of these are really necessary. We also need an arrow to show the way to the restaurant.

We can combine these symbols in a sketch of the proposed sign, and experiment with various colour combinations. The ideas can be tested by asking other people to read them.

A good method of producing your final design is to draw and cut out the symbols using, for example, black paper, and glue them on to paper of the background colour.

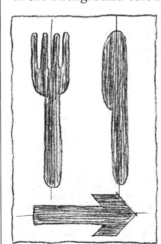

Design sketch

Finished design

59

ACTIVITIES

1 Using the method of designing the restaurant symbol as a guide, design and produce similar signs for these areas of the department store:

- toys
- holiday bookings
- unisex hair styling
- records and audio cassettes
- men's clothes
- women's clothes.

The signs are to be hung from the ceilings, and should be the same size and shape.

2 A national newspaper carries regular reports of sporting events. The symbols shown are used to indicate which sport each report is about.

Design similar symbols to represent these sports:

- cricket
- hockey
- football
- table tennis
- skiing.

The printed symbols are 20mm square. Draw your finished designs to a scale of 5:1, using white shapes mounted on black paper.

badminton

swimming

rowing

cycling

weightlifting

3 The photograph shows a TV weather forecast in progress.

From the map and symbols, write a short, clear summary of the forecast.

Compare your written summary with the map. Which is quicker and easier to read?

Design similar weather symbols, each inside a 100mm square, to represent:

- a fierce storm
- wind (showing direction and strength)
- snow
- fog.

TV weather forecast

4 A computer magazine publishes reviews of software which can be bought for various computers.

The software can be stored on a cassette tape, on a floppy disc or on a ROM (Read Only Memory) chip. The photograph shows one of each.

The magazine editor wants you to design symbols representing tape, disc and ROM. Some of the these will be displayed at the top of each review, to show the type of storage used.

The editor wants each symbol inside a rectangle 15mm wide and 20mm high. Draw your final design to a scale of 5:1.

Cassette, floppy disc and ROM

5 Below is an entry in a book about camp sites in Britain.

It gives directions for getting to the site, the number of places available for caravans, motor caravans and tents and prices for staying one night.

The symbols represent facilities available at the site. Write a list of as many of the facilities as you can.

Invent a name and details of a camp site from your imagination. Write an entry for it similar to the one shown. Include small ink sketches of symbols for the facilities.

Llanberis
Gwynedd   Map 6C1

Snowdon View Caravan Park
Brynrefail, Llanberis LL45 3PD. Tel: Llanberis (0286) 870349. From Caernarvon take A4086 5 miles (8km) east. Then take A4547 Banger Road north for 0.75 miles (1.5km). Site located on right. Signposted. 28 acres (11 hec). Grassy and level. Extra charges for caravan awnings.
Open Mar - Oct.

    68 🚐 £3.00 - 5.00
    25 🚐 £2.00 - 4.00
  150 ⛺ £1.50 - 3.50

Logos

A logo is a symbol or group of letters which create a **visual identity** for a firm or an organisation. Logos are used in advertisements, letter headings and on buildings and vehicles. As with signs and symbols, the designs should be bold and simple, yet striking in appearance.

Some logos are based on letters linked together to form a single design. These are called **monograms**.

Other logos use initials or a name inside a geometrical shape.

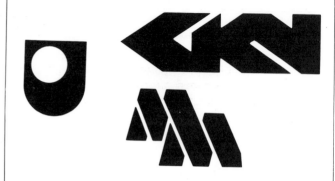

Monograms

Another type of logo uses **pictorial symbols** to convey a basic **idea** about what a firm or organisation does. The name of the organisation is sometimes included in the design. Can you identify those opposite?

Save the Children
A shampoo manufacturer
Plessey Electronics
Surrey County Council
Oxfam
A clothes shop
A sports equipment manufacturer
Doctor Barnardo's
British Rail

Logos using geometrical shapes

Logos using pictorial symbols

ACTIVITIES

1 Collect display logos from advertisements in newspapers and magazines. Sort them into the types described on the previous page. Mount and display them on coloured paper.

2 Design a logo for Channel 5 TV.

3 Collect the names of all the clubs that are run in your school.

Design a suitable logo for some or all of the clubs. Compare and discuss your finished designs.

Perhaps you can persuade each club to adopt the logo of their choice?

4 Design a logo using your initials inside a hexagon.

Shape the letters to fit the hexagon in both possible positions. Use the sketches shown here as a guide.

You can link your initials to form a monogram if you wish. Explore different ways in which you could do this. Include colour in your sketches.

Draw your final design on A4 cartridge paper, using a hexagon 120mm A/F (across flats).

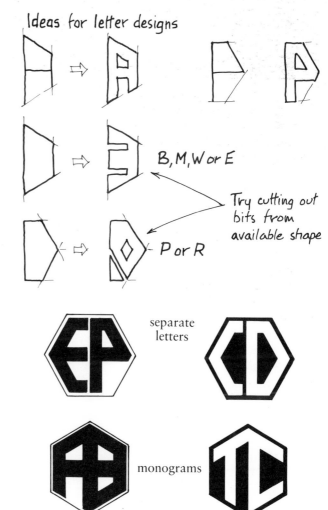

Ideas for letter designs

B, M, W or E

Try cutting out bits from available shape

P or R

separate letters

monograms

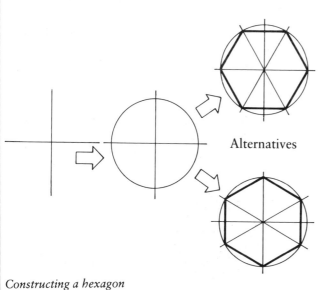

Constructing a hexagon

Alternatives

Designing letters for a hexagonal logo

Letter design

Lettering is often specially designed to emphasise the meaning of a word.

Letter design is important in shop names, advertising, titles of TV programmes, posters, magazines and newspapers. The examples opposite are from the Letraset range of dry transfer lettering.

The design of the letters must suit the meaning of the word, or the use being made of it. The title of a comic needs a bold, colourful design like 'Frankfurter'. Which design would you use to advertise a film called 'Dracula Strikes Again'?

Square grid sheets are useful for sketching ideas for letter designs. Keep your designs simple so you can work out how to draw them using instruments if possible.

Shop names

Magazine titles

Block Up
ABCDEFGHIJKLMN
1234567890

Cirkulus
abcdefghijklmnopqrstuv
1234567890

Data 70
abcdefghijklmnopqrstuvw
1234567890

Frankfurter Medium
aabcdefghijklmnopqrst
1234567890

Good Vibrations
ABCDEFGHIJKLMN
1234567890

Neon
ABCDEFGHIJKLMNOP
1234567890

Romantiques No.5
ABCDEFGHIJKLM
WXYZ

Shatter
abcdefghijklmnopqrst
1234567890

Sunshine
abcdefghijklmnopqrstu
1234567890

Traffic
abcdefghijklmnopqqr
1234567890

Some letter styles from the Letraset catalogue

ACTIVITIES

1 The sketch shows ideas for letter designs for various words. The impression of movement in FAST, for example, is conveyed by the horizontal lines, and by sloping the letters forward.

Sketch ideas for letter designs to suit these words:

sharp, power, puddle, rain, strong, whisper, your name

Make up other words of your own if you wish.

Draw each word, using instruments if possible, in the letter style you have designed.

2 Choose one of the Letraset designs on the previous page to suit each of the following:

- Big Top – the name of a circus on an advertising poster
- Sounds Amazing – the name of a hi-fi shop
- Starbright – the name above the door of a nightclub
- Hacker – the title of a computer magazine
- Elegance – the name on the label of a bottle of perfume.

Draw the letters of each word using the examples given as a guide. Carefully ink in the letters, using a ruler where possible.

You will have to design in the same style any letters not shown. Perhaps you can borrow a Letraset catalogue?

3 House numbers should be clear yet distinctive. Sketch or trace the house number on your front door or gate. Note how it is fixed, and the material from which it is made.

Sketch a series of alternative ideas for the design of your house number. What size should the numbers be?

Draw your final design full size, showing the method of fixing, and the material used.

7 | Showing information

Bar charts

Bar charts are a clear way of **comparing quantities**. Each bar chart should be designed to communicate the given information as clearly as possible.

They should include all necessary written information – a title, what each bar represents, and the scale.

Brief: design a bar chart which compares the populations of five major cities.

The examples below are all solutions to this brief. Which do you think is the best solution?

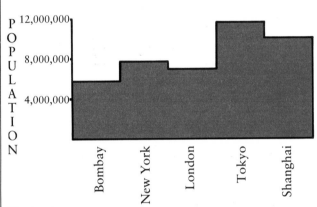

Version 1

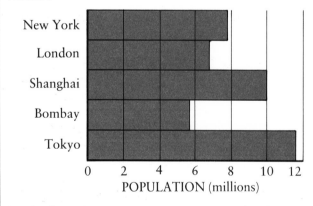

Version 2

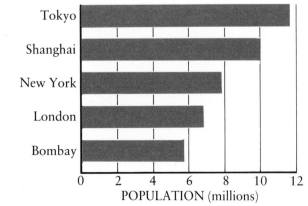

An effective test for a bar chart is to try to read it. According to the brief, the chart should be able to tell us:

- Which is the city with the third highest population?
- What is the approximate population of Shanghai?
- What is the approximate population of the smallest city?

Try to answer these questions, using each chart in turn.

The best designed bar chart can supply the answers quickly and easily because:

- the bars are arranged in order of length
- the design is simple and uncluttered
- the words can be read without turning your head
- each bar is separate and clearly labelled.

Treat each design brief as a new problem. Sketch and compare various layouts before drawing a final version to scale.

These population charts are called **simple** bar charts. An example of a **compound** bar chart is shown below. Compound bar charts compare two or more groups within the same category.

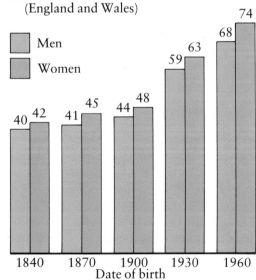

A compound bar chart

Version 3

ACTIVITIES

1 Here is a list of the World Football Cup winners since 1930:

1930	Uruguay
1934	Italy
1938	Italy
1950	Uruguay
1954	West Germany
1958	Brazil
1962	Brazil
1966	England
1970	Brazil
1974	West Germany
1978	Argentina
1982	Italy
1986	Argentina

Design a bar chart to show the number of times each country has won the Cup.

England vs. Morocco 1986

2 Do a survey of your CDT group to find how many of you travel to school in each of the following ways:

walking
bus
cycle
car
other

Design a bar chart to show this information.

In which order will you draw the bars on your chart? Why?

3 Write a list of ten different foods, some of which you like and some of which you do not like.

Give each food a score up to +5 if you like it, and down to −5 if you do not like it.

Examples: Rhubarb +4 (I like it very much)
Tomatoes 0 (I am neutral about them)
Marmalade −2 (I would rather not eat it)

Design a bar chart to show this information. How can you show both positive and negative values?

4 Farmers around the world look after more than 10 000 million animals. Here are the numbers of some of them:

Horses	62m
Cows	1 215m
Pigs	730m
Turkeys	90m
Sheep	1 044m
Goats	435m
Chickens	6 500m

Design a bar chart to show the numbers of these animals.

If you draw a scale to allow for the 6 500m chickens, the bars for the horses and turkeys will be so short, they will not show up.

Rather than draw a scale at the side or bottom of your chart, you could try printing the number above each bar.

5 Find some interesting statistics about your favourite hobby (e.g. sport, model making, films, stamp collecting, computers).

Present this information in the form of a bar chart.

Pie charts

Pie charts are an effective way of showing **how something is shared.**

The share of each item is shown as a different sized slice of the 'pie'. If you know the percentage of each item, you can work out the angle of each slice by multiplying the percentage by 3.6.

e.g. Angle for USSR slice (below) = 24 × 3.6 = 86.4°.

An easier way is to use a **circular percentage chart** to measure each angle. This is an instrument like a protractor but has the circle divided into 100.

Print the name and percentage of each item on the slice if there is enough space. Otherwise, colour code each slice and draw a key, as in the example below.

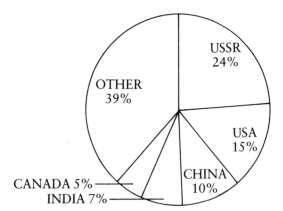

Where the world's wheat is grown

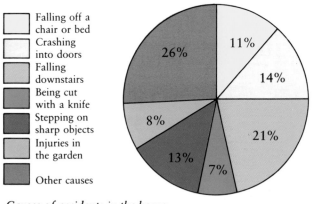

Causes of accidents in the home

Line graphs

Line graphs, like bar charts, are a way of **comparing quantities.**

Unlike bar charts, line graphs show a **continuous** comparison. In the graph below, we can read the speed of the rocket at any time after take off.

Where curves are needed, they are best drawn using a French curve.

If there are several lines, they can be labelled on the graph, or colour coded as shown here.

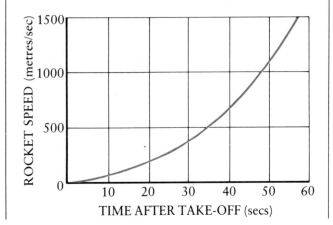

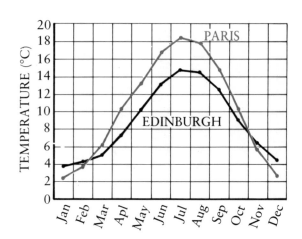

ACTIVITIES

1 From the charts and graphs on the previous page, answer the following:

- What is the biggest single cause of accidents in the home?
- Which country grows twice as much wheat as Canada?
- What is the approximate speed of the rocket 25 seconds after take-off?
- How long after take-off does the rocket reach 500m/sec?
- Is Paris or Edinburgh the warmest city for most of the winter?
- How much warmer is Paris than Edinburgh in September?

2 Here are the main countries which grow rice, and the percentage which each grows:

China	35%
India	20%
Indonesia	6%
Bangladesh	5%
Japan	5%
Other	29%

Draw a pie chart to show this information.

3 Look at the information from the survey you did in Activity 2 on page 67. Draw a pie chart to show what proportion of your CDT group use the various ways of coming to school.

You will have to calculate the percentage of each group. Here is an example to help you:

Number ($\times$ 100 $\div$ 16) $\rightarrow$ Percentage

Walking	3	18.75%
Bus	6	37.50%
Cycle	4	25.00%
Car	2	12.50%
Other	1	6.25%
Total	16	100.00%

Then calculate the angles, or use a circular percentage chart.

Print the percentages on your pie chart.

4 The table below shows the popularity of some girls' and boys' names during the last hundred years.

Registered names for each 10 000 births of the same sex

	1875	1900	1925	1950	1975
Barbara	3	13	162	216	2
Helen	25	27	26	58	226
Lucy	95	61	22	4	71
Robert	231	267	284	356	231
Frank	136	206	196	34	10
Philip	25	22	40	174	107

Design a line graph to show this information.

From your graph, find the following:

- the most popular of the boys' names in 1975
- the least popular of the girls' names in 1950
- which girls' names are getting more popular
- which boys' names are getting less popular.

Pictorial charts

The simplest design usually makes the clearest chart. However, there are many ways to make them more interesting and attractive.

One way to make bar charts and pie charts interesting is to draw them in oblique projection, like the ones shown here. Pictorial charts can also look attractive as illustrations in their own right.

Clever techniques can be used to make charts contain a lot of information. The chart below is based on a map of Britain. The **size** of each block represents the population of the area. The **colour** represents how quickly the population is growing or declining.

STAND UP AND BE COUNTED

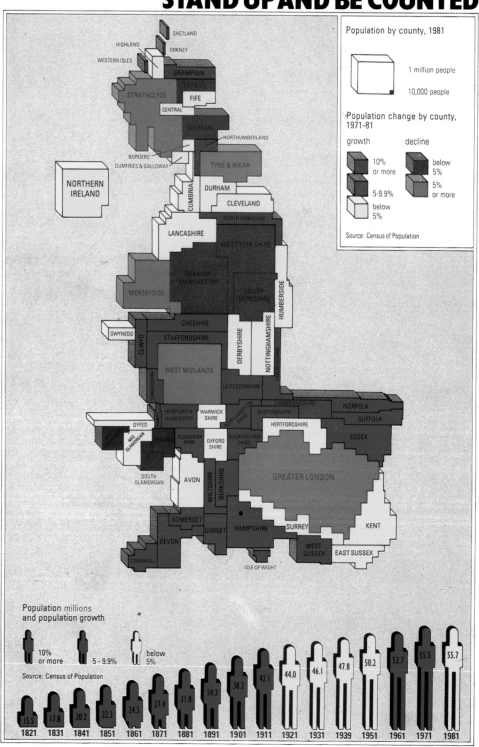

Using symbols can add impact to the meaning of a chart. The missile symbol used as bars in the chart on military spending is an example of this.

In the 'Scenic Spoils' chart, the bars are also symbols of what is happening in each area.

Once you have confidence in designing simple charts, start using more imagination in your designs. Remember, though, that the aim of any chart is to present information clearly.

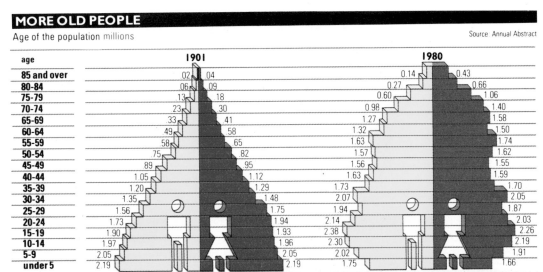

MORE OLD PEOPLE

Age of the population millions

Source: Annual Abstract

HEIRS TO THE THRONE

Sources of energy consumed percentages

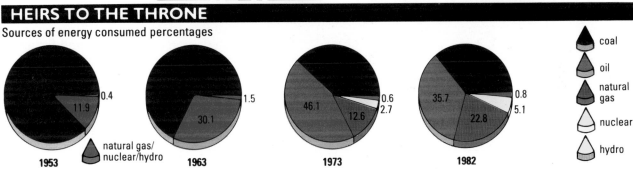

coal
oil
natural gas
nuclear
hydro

Sources: Annual Abstract; Energy Trends

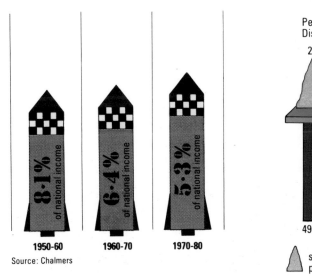

Source: Chalmers

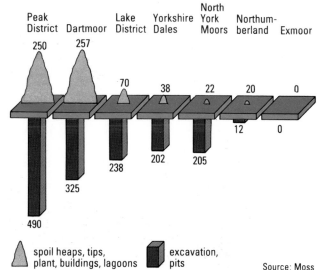

spoil heaps, tips, plant, buildings, lagoons

excavation, pits

Source: Moss

Giving directions

Directions are sometimes needed to explain how to make or do something. A **flow diagram** shows these directions in stages.

Flow diagrams can use illustrations, symbols, words, or a mixture of these. Here are two versions of a simple one:

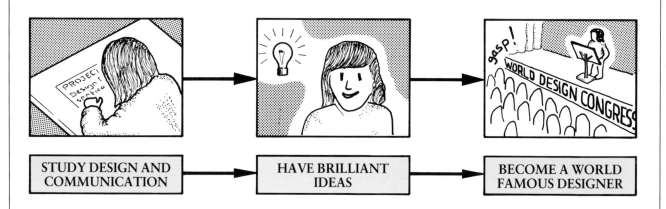

STUDY DESIGN AND COMMUNICATION	→	HAVE BRILLIANT IDEAS	→	BECOME A WORLD FAMOUS DESIGNER

Other examples can be found in earlier chapters in this book. Try to find them.

The sequence is often shown by arrows, which should flow from left to right, or from top to bottom. Numbered stages can also be used.

You have probably seen or used flow diagrams, for example on a drinks or snacks machine, or for making plastic models from a kit of parts. Can you think of other examples?

Words are good enough for simple directions, but complicated ones need symbols or illustrations to make them clear.

Passengers in an aircraft may need to know very quickly how to fit a life jacket in an emergency. Words would take too long to read, and fitting a life jacket is difficult to describe. Can you think of another reason for not using words in this case?

Fitting an aircraft life jacket

GILET DE SAUVETAGE / LIFE JACKET
RETTUNGSWESTE / CHALECO SALVAVIDAS

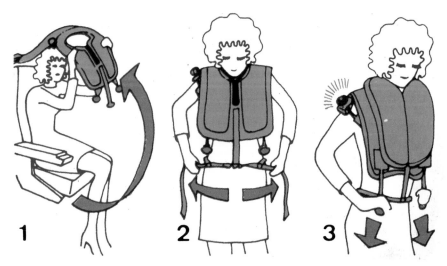

Ne gonflez votre gilet qu'après en avoir reçu l'ordre
Wait for crew order before inflating your jacket
Schwimmweste erst dann aufblasen, wenn Sie dazu aufgefordert werden
No infle su chaleco antes de recibir la orden correspondiente

ACTIVITY

1 Here is the start of a flow diagram showing how to play a record. Write down the remaining stages – including putting the record away after playing it.

Copy the flow diagram as drawn but use a vertical layout. Use your notes to complete the diagram.

2 The drawings below show stages of a flow diagram in the wrong order. Some of the stages are shown as symbols, and some as words.

Arrange the stages in the correct order and redraw them as a flow diagram. Copy the symbols used and replace the words with symbols of your own design. Add a suitable title.

3 It can be difficult to remember how to set the time on a digital watch. It is usually done by pushing buttons in a certain order with a ballpoint pen.

The drawing opposite could be used in each stage of a flow diagram explaining how to set the time. A short instruction, pointing at the right button, is needed at each stage.

Sketch a suitable flow diagram which explains how to set your watch. Test it by asking other people to say what it means. Produce a finished drawing of your flow diagram.

If you are not sure how to set you watch, now is the time to find out!

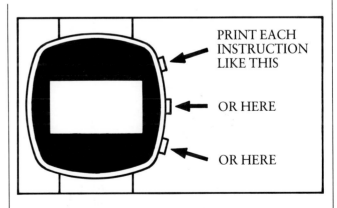

Making decisions

So far we have only considered a fixed sequence of events (one thing happening after another). But some actions are more complicated than this.

Think about one thing some of us are not very good at – getting out of bed in the morning! The flow diagram could look like this:

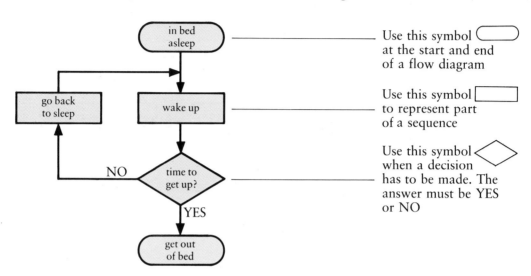

Use this symbol at the start and end of a flow diagram

Use this symbol to represent part of a sequence

Use this symbol when a decision has to be made. The answer must be YES or NO

Using symbols in flow diagrams

The next flow diagram shows a machine, rather than a person, making decisions. The machine sorts potatoes into large, medium and small sizes.

The diagram does not show how the machine works – only what it does. Designers use diagrams like this when designing a complicated machine which has to perform many operations. This is also a method of designing computer programs.

Flow diagram for a potato sorting machine

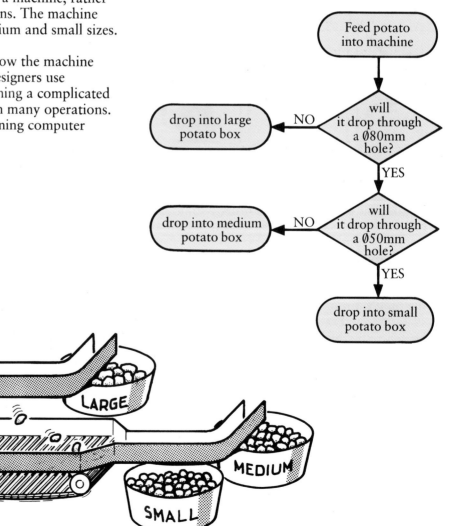

ACTIVITY

Noughts and crosses is one of the oldest games in the world. Variations of it were played in ancient China, Greece and Rome.

If neither player makes a mistake, the result should be a draw. This is done by playing to certain rules. Have you ever thought what these rules are?

If you play each turn according to this flow diagram, you should never lose. The diagram has three stages, which can be written down like this:

Stage 1: If I can win by going in a square, go there.

Stage 2: If my opponent would win on his next turn by going in a square, go there to stop him.

Stage 3: If neither of these apply, go to a square which has the most lines going through it.

Try playing a few games using the diagram each time. Each stage is very easy, although it will seem slow until you get used to it. You may find that you have always played this way, without really thinking about it!

Once you understand how this diagram works, design a flow diagram to help you play one of these games:

- Connect 4 (the 'vertical strategy' game)
- Dots (drawing lines to make squares on a grid of dots)
- Dominoes

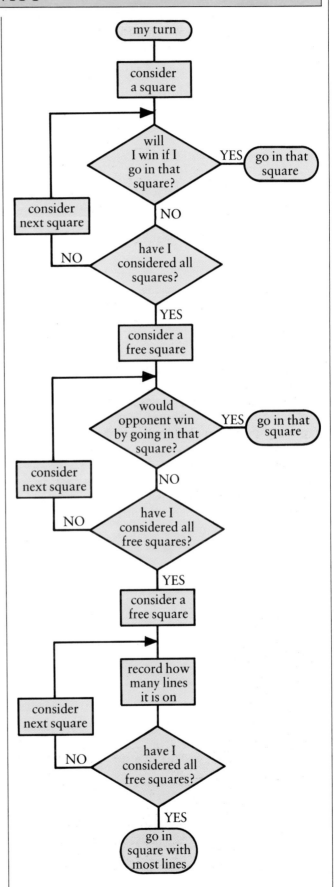

8 | Maps and plans

Maps

An aerial photograph shows an area of land in great detail, but it can be difficult to find the information you are looking for. This is an aerial view of Colchester.

Maps are designed to show particular kinds of information very clearly. Details which are not needed are left out.

Road maps and **street** maps show motorists and pedestrians where places are, and how to get to them.

In **schematic** maps the chosen features are shown in a simplified form. A 'How to find us' map, like the one shown here, is a typical example. The map is not to scale.

Schematic maps are often used to show bus or train routes, such as the well-known map of the London Underground.

Symbols can be used on maps to show where useful or interesting places are. This map shows places of interest in North Wales.

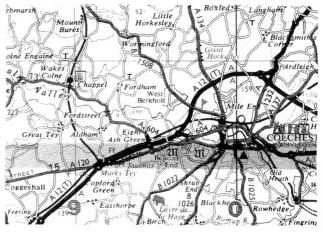

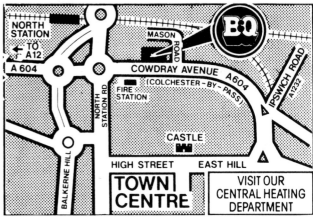

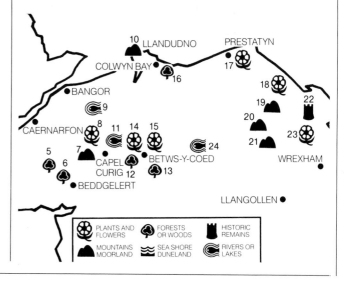

ACTIVITIES

1 You are sending invitations to a party. Some of your friends live a long way from you and do not know your area.

Draw a map of the streets around your home, using a street map or from memory. Add the words PARTY HERE together with the date and time. Print this information inside a box, with an arrow pointing to your house.

2 This is a road map for motorists who want to travel through Huddersfield. It shows the main 'A' roads and very little else.

Find your town or village in an atlas. Trace or copy the main features only, and draw a similar road map showing the main roads.

3 You have been asked by the local tourist information office to design a map for visitors, showing places of interest in your town.

From a street map, draw a schematic map showing the main roads only. Design symbols for interesting places such as castles, museums, parks and historic buildings.

Add these symbols to your map, and a key explaining what the symbols mean.

4 This is an imaginary island off the south coast of England. It is to become 'Leisure Island' offering outdoor facilities.

Here are some suggested facilities: boat hire, swimming, horse riding, picnic area, open air concerts, footpaths for walks, danger signs where needed.

Design a map showing the facilities you think should be offered. You could use symbols, or any other method you think suitable.

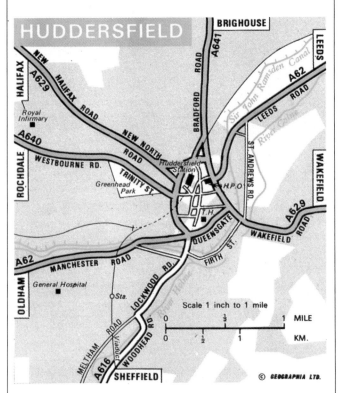

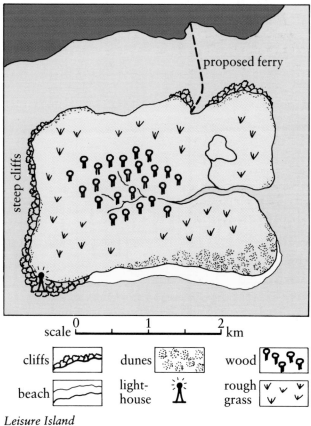

Leisure Island

Site plans

Site plans are drawn to a larger scale than maps. They show less land, but more detail such as buildings, walls, pathways and trees.

Site plans are useful for showing the layout of a collection of buildings such as a housing estate, a new town centre, a school or a farm.

The position and appearance of new buildings needs careful planning. They are expensive to build, and people have to live and work in and around them for many years.

The illustration below shows a street scene of planned new houses. Can you find each house on the site plan underneath?

The direction of north is shown using the symbol ①. Why should it be important to show the direction of north?

Typical scales used for site plans are 1:1250, 1:500 and 1:200.

Street scene

Site plan

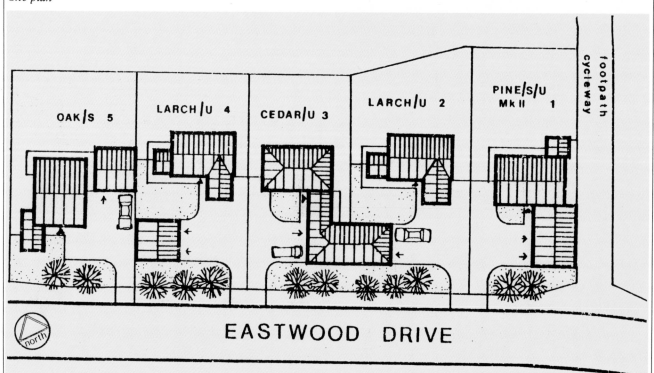

ACTIVITIES

1 Sketch a rough plan of your house and garden like the one shown. Include features such as a garage, shed, greenhouse and paths if you have them.

Measure the most important distances by pacing. For example, your house may be 15 paces wide and 28 paces front to back. Mark these on your sketch.

Using a square grid and a scale of 1 pace = 5mm, draw a plan of your house and garden.

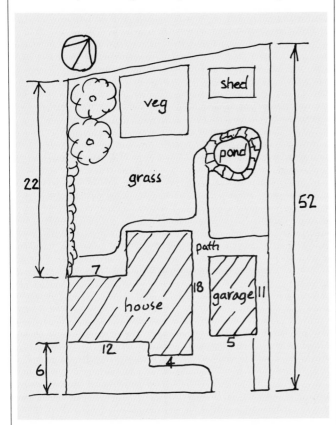

2 What would your ideal school be like? Here is your chance to design it.

Some facilities must be included, such as a dining hall, classrooms, toilets and a cycle rack.

Other facilities can be included because you want them, such as a swimming pool, sports hall, computer games room or just quiet places to sit.

Make a list of facilities you think your school must have, and another list of facilities you would like.

Produce sketches of ideas for the layout, and then a final drawing. Include all the facilities you have listed. Indicate the use of each building, e.g. science block, dining hall.

3 The plan shows a supermarket and car park. Redraw this plan twice the size shown. The scale of your plan will then be 1:200.

The car park needs to be divided into marked parking spaces. Each parking space should measure 5m × 2.5m.

The maximum number of parking spaces is needed, whilst allowing cars to get in and out easily.

Sketch different layouts, using bank paper on top of your plan of the car park. Alternatively, experiment using pieces of card cut to the scale size of a parking space.

Draw your best layout of parking spaces to the correct scale on your plan.

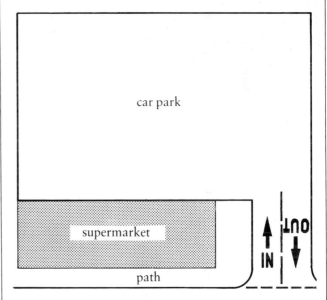

Building plans

Building plans show the shape and size of each room, and the positions of doors and windows. They may also show such things as furniture, radiators, light switches and power points.

The building plan below shows both floors of a new house. Notice the kitchen and bathroom fittings, and the open doors. Why are the doors shown open?

Compare the building plan with the illustration of the house. Can you match the doors and windows on both drawings?

The outside walls are thick because they are really two walls with a cavity (space) between them. The cavity stops rain reaching the inside wall, and helps to insulate the house.

Useful scales for building plans are 1:100 and 1:50.

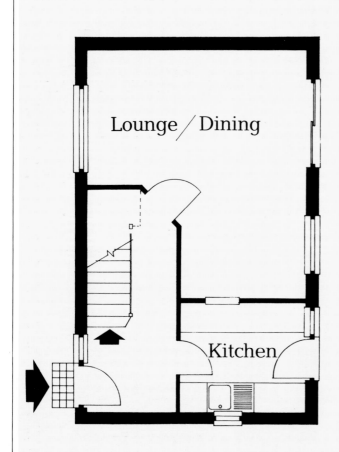
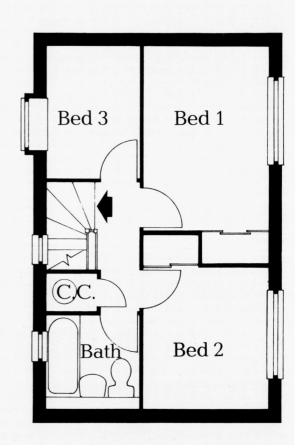

Compare this building plan with the illustration above

ACTIVITIES

1 Some dimensions are the same in most houses. Knowing these dimensions will help you to draw your own building plans.

Measure and record these dimensions in your house. Use a steel measuring tape, or a cloth measuring tape as used in dressmaking.

Item	Dimensions (metres)	
Internal doors	width	height ....
External doors	width	height ....
Internal wall	thickness	
External wall	thickness	
Stairs	width of treads	
Bath	width	length ....
Wash basin	width	depth ....
Toilet and cistern	width	depth ....
Kitchen units	height	depth ....
Single bed	width	length ....
Double bed	width	length ....

2 Draw a sketch of one or more rooms in your house, including the furniture. Measure the most important dimensions and record these on your sketch.

From your sketch, draw an accurate plan of the room or rooms, using a scale of 1:50. Include the furniture and any other details you think important.

3 This plan shows the outside walls of a proposed bungalow, without the doors and windows. This plan has been designed to suit the plot of land available.

The owner would like these rooms in the bungalow:

hall
sitting room
kitchen/dining room
bathroom
two bedrooms.

Complete the specification with these points, and others of your own:

- at least two external doors are needed
- each room needs at least one window
- there should be easy access to each room.

Sketch some possible layouts for the rooms, using square grid paper and a suitable scale.

Draw an accurate plan of your best layout to a scale of 1:50. Use the dimensions you recorded in Activity 1 to help you.

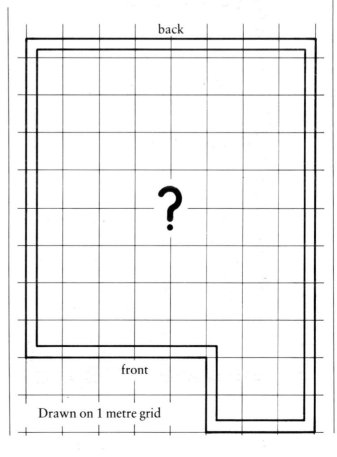

back

?

front

Drawn on 1 metre grid

81

9 | Computer aided design

Computer technology is still very young, even younger than electronics. Micro-computers that many people could afford to buy have only been available since the late 1970s. They have since been rapidly developed and improved. This development is still going on. In ten years time, computers will be immensely powerful compared with those of today.

This chapter will tell you how computers work, and how you can use different types of CAD (Computer Aided Design) software. Start by studying the illustration below. Name and describe the equipment available to your CDT group.

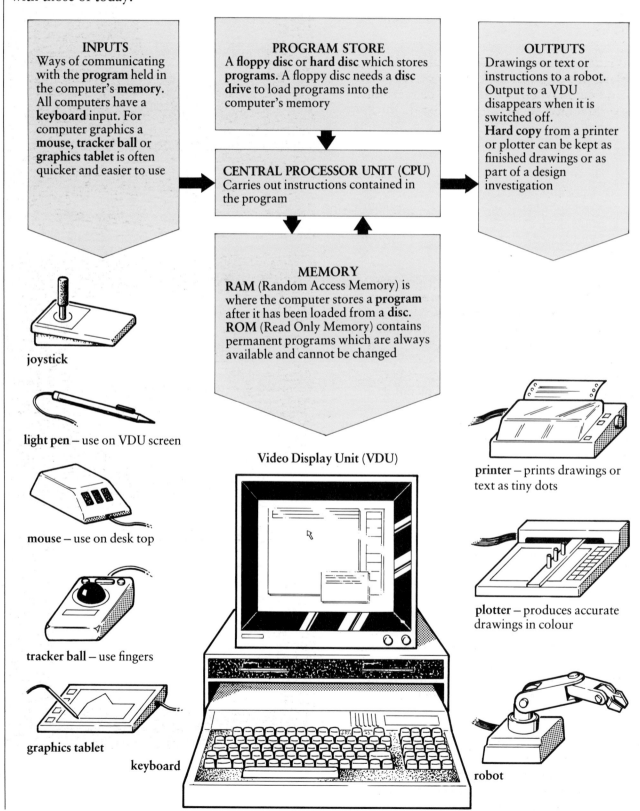

INPUTS
Ways of communicating with the **program** held in the computer's **memory**. All computers have a **keyboard** input. For computer graphics a **mouse, tracker ball** or **graphics tablet** is often quicker and easier to use

PROGRAM STORE
A **floppy disc** or **hard disc** which stores **programs**. A floppy disc needs a **disc drive** to load programs into the computer's memory

OUTPUTS
Drawings or text or instructions to a robot. Output to a VDU disappears when it is switched off.
Hard copy from a printer or plotter can be kept as finished drawings or as part of a design investigation

CENTRAL PROCESSOR UNIT (CPU)
Carries out instructions contained in the program

MEMORY
RAM (Random Access Memory) is where the computer stores a **program** after it has been loaded from a **disc**.
ROM (Read Only Memory) contains permanent programs which are always available and cannot be changed

joystick

light pen – use on VDU screen

mouse – use on desk top

tracker ball – use fingers

graphics tablet

keyboard

Video Display Unit (VDU)

printer – prints drawings or text as tiny dots

plotter – produces accurate drawings in colour

robot

Draughting

Some CAD software replaces the drawing board and instruments altogether. At the top of the VDU screen is a set of **icons** – symbols for a straight line, circle, rectangle, printing, hatching and so on. You move a **pointer** (a small arrow) on the screen using a mouse. You select and place icons anywhere on the screen and quickly create a drawing.

This kind of software is suitable for producing working drawings, circuit diagrams or printed circuit board layouts. Designs can be saved on a disc or 'dumped' to a printer or plotter.

Simulations

Simulations carry out complicated calculations to do with designing. For example, when designing an aircraft, engineers have to decide the dimensions of many thousands of parts, and the material to use. Without a computer it would take teams of engineers many days to work out whether the structure would be safe in flight. A computer can do this quickly and reliably.

Simulations can predict the top speed of a car before it is built, how much a tall building will sway in a high wind and how much payload a rocket can launch into orbit.

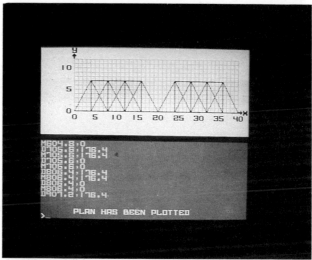

3-D views

One way of checking the appearance of a design is to make a scale model. Another way is to use the computer to draw the design from many different viewpoints.

Large computers used by TV stations and in industry can produce spectacular, detailed images in full colour, and animate them as well. This takes more memory than a school computer has, but you should be able to produce 'wire frame' drawings of simple objects.

The design can be changed quickly and easily. You can rotate it, produce a mirror image, alter the scale and join shapes together. By tracing and colouring printouts, you can produce design sketches or finished illustrations.

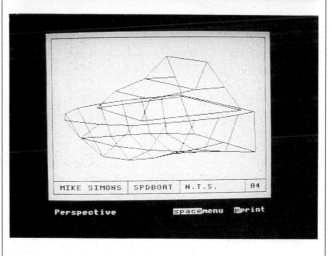

Robots

Automatic machines, such as traffic lights, have existed for many years. Computer controlled robots, however, are **programmed** to carry out a sequence of tasks. By changing the program, the same robot can carry out different tasks.

Robots are especially useful for doing things which are difficult, dangerous or boring for people to do. They can weld vehicle bodies, spray paint, work in icy conditions, and they never get tired!

Computer Aided Manufacture (CAM) can make working drawings unnecessary. For example, a computer controlled lathe can produce gearbox shafts directly from a program containing all the necessary instructions.

In school, you may be able to use a **turtle**, a small wheeled robot, programmed using a computer language called Logo. Other educational robots are becoming available, which are capable of performing similar tasks to industrial robots.

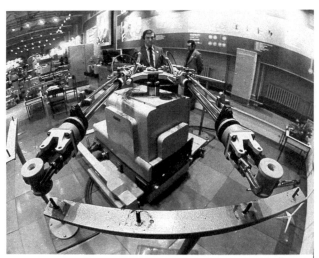

An industrial robot

Computer art

This software helps you produce freehand drawings on the VDU screen, and print them. As well as drawing shapes such as circles and rectangles, you can 'paint' with 'brushes' of different thicknesses, in a choice of colours. You can fill an area with colour or a choice of patterns, or 'cut' part of a drawing and 'paste' it somewhere else. You can even use an 'airbrush' to give a stippled effect to drawings.

These programs often use an input system called WIMP, meaning Windows, Icons, Mouse, and Pointer. Using a mouse needs only one hand and is easy to learn. Sometimes a lightpen, which draws directly on the VDU screen, is used instead. A designer can use this type of program to produce illustrations or design sketches.

Databases

A database is like a computerised encyclopedia. By using a **modem** attached to a computer, you can look up information about almost any subject on a national database such as Prestel. Modems use telephone lines to communicate with databases, and the information is always up to date.

This can be useful for doing research on a design project. A well-designed database is easy to use and 'intelligent' – it will answer questions about what you are looking for. This and other information can be saved on a disc. In this way you can create your own database, which can be added to and altered to suit your needs.

The computer can draw graphs and charts automatically from information in the database. It can quickly search for and find the information you want, and rearrange it in alphabetical or numerical order. The information can be printed out at any time.

Wordprocessing

Designing often involves writing reports, specifications and evaluations. Using a wordprocessor to do this has many advantages. It is easy to change words or sentences, move paragraphs, and 'format' your text. Some wordprocessors can even check your spelling! You no longer need to re-write a rough copy using pen and paper. The printer will produce perfect copies for you.

You can produce titles and notes for your drawings on a printer too, using large print or special **fonts** (letter styles). These can be cut from a printout and mounted on your drawings. There are other software packages which help you to design magazines or leaflets, by mixing text and graphics.

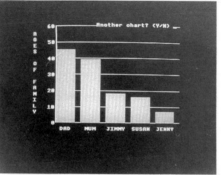

Computer characters program

The VDU screen is divided into tiny squares called pixels. A block of 8 × 8 pixels is needed to display each of the characters on the keyboard, as well as 'user defined' characters which you can design yourself.

Each character has an ASCII number. You can find these in the computer user guide. User defined characters start at ASCII number 224. Using this program, you can display an enlarged view of any character and print it on a printer.

Type the listing below into the computer, and SAVE the program as 'CHARS'. After the program is RUN initially, you can press ESCAPE to list it, and press f1 (red key) to RUN it again. At this stage you can display all the standard characters (ASCII numbers 33 to 126).

Design your own characters on an 8 × 8 square grid. (See page 13 for some ideas.) Work out the 8-number code for each design, as shown in the example on the next page. List the program to add a line giving the computer details of each user defined character.

SAVE the program at the end of the lesson. Use a different filename (e.g. CHARS1, CHARS2 etc.) for each CDT group. Before using the printer, make sure it is connected and 'on line'.

```
10 REM Large Character Display
20 REM Brian Light 1987
30 REM BBC B/Master + Epson printer
40 ON ERROR GOTO 730
50 *KEY0 L.|M
60 *KEY1    RUN|M
70 PROCreadchars
80 X%=285:Y%=850:S%=70
90 REPEAT:MODE4
100 PROCinput
110 PROCdisplay
120 UNTIL FALSE
130
140 DEFPROCinput
150 VDU23,255,0,8,8,8,8,8,8,0
160 VDU24,0;160;1274;1024;
170 VDU28,0,31,39,26
180 c1%=7:c2%=4
190 VDU19,0,c1%,0,0,0,19,7,c2%,0,0,0
200 PROCgrid
210 PRINTTAB(0,3)"To define a new char
acter: press ESCAPE"
220 INPUTTAB(0,0)"To see your characte
r design: type the  ASCII number then pr
ess RETURN "ascno%
230 CLS:IF ascno%<32 OR ascno%>255 VDU
7:GOTO210
240 ENDPROC
250
260 DEFPROCdisplay
270 PRINTTAB(9,0)"Character number ";a
scno%;TAB(3,2);"Press SPACE BAR to inver
t colours"
280 PRINTTAB(3,3);"Press RETURN for an
other character"'"    Press P to print"
290 VDU5:MOVE800,1000:PRINT"Actual siz
e ";CHR$(ascno%):VDU4
300 PROCchar(ascno%)
310 *KEY1 |MRUN|M
320 REPEAT:G$=GET$
330 IF ASC(G$)=32 c1%=c1%EOR3:c2%=c2%E
OR3:VDU19,0,c1%,0,0,0,19,7,c2%,0,0,0
340 IF ASC(G$)=80 PROCprint
350 UNTIL ASC(G$)=13
360 ENDPROC
370
380 DEFPROCgrid
390 h%=295:VDU5
400 FOR v%=300 TO 860 STEP 70
```

```
410 MOVE h%,v%:VDU45
420 MOVE h%+595,v%:VDU45:NEXT
430 v%=280
440 FOR h%=310 TO 870 STEP 70
450 MOVE h%,v%:VDU255
460 MOVE h%,v%+600:VDU255:NEXT
470 VDU4:ENDPROC
480
490 DEFPROCchar(chrno%)
500 IF chrno%>223 PROCread ELSE A%=&BF
00+chrno%*8
510 FOR P%=0 TO 7:FOR Q%=0 TO 7
520 MOVE X%-Q%*S%+7.6*S%,Y%-P%*S%
530 IF(2^Q% AND A%?P%)<>0 PLOT 0,S%,0:
PLOT81,-S%,-S%:PLOT 81,S%,0
540 NEXT:NEXT
550 ENDPROC
560
570 DEFPROCread
580 LOCAL X%,Y%
590 Y%=&B:?&B00=chrno%
600 A%=10:CALL&FFF1:A%=&B01
610 ENDPROC
620
630 DEFPROCprint
640 VDU2,1,27,1,51,1,24
650 FOR C%=&5800 TO &5938 STEP 8
660 VDU1,27,1,42,1,5,1,0,1,1
670 FOR A%=C%+&26C0 TO C% STEP -320
680 FOR B%=A%+7 TO A% STEP -1
690 VDU1,?B%:NEXT:NEXT
700 VDU1,13,1,10:NEXT:VDU3,7
710 ENDPROC
720
730 ON ERROR OFF:MODE7
740 OSCLI("K.OL."+"|M")
750 *FX138,0,128
760 END
770
780 DEFPROCreadchars
790 REM*************************
800 REM Add a new line below and type
       the VDU 23 code for your own
       character: example given.
       Then press RETURN.
       Then press red key f1.
810 VDU23,224,28,28,8,127,8,20,34,65
2000 ENDPROC
```

How to define your own character

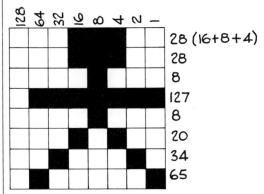

ASCII number 224

28 (16+8+4)
28
8
127
8
20
34
65

Complete code to define this character:
VDU 23, 224, 28, 28, 8, 127, 8, 20, 34, 65
(See line 810 in program listing)

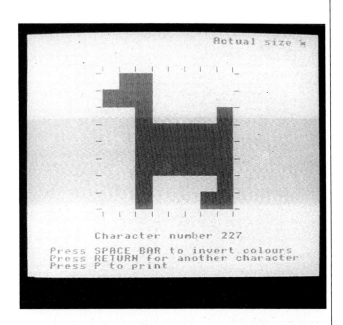

Character number 227
Press SPACE BAR to invert colours
Press RETURN for another character
Press P to print

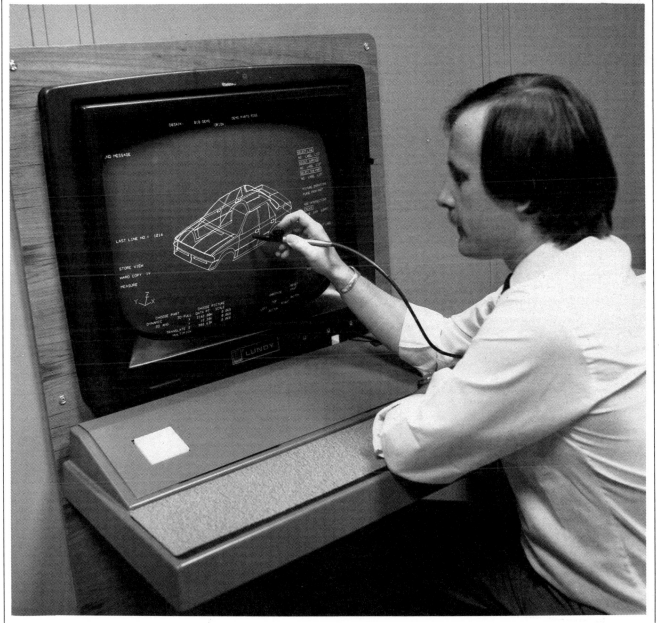

10 | Design projects

Each design project in this chapter will take several lessons to complete. Your teacher will probably set a deadline, so you will have to plan each stage of your work.

Each project starts with some **background information** which describes the problem to be tackled. You are then given a **brief,** and hints for tackling each stage of the design process. Read pages 6 and 7 again carefully to remind yourself what the stages are, and what each stage is about.

Careful **presentation** of your project work is very important because:

- it helps you to think clearly
- it helps you remember where you left off at the end of the last lesson
- it preserves a record of your work that anyone can look at and understand
- it give you a sense of pride in your work.

A folder can be simply a sheet of A3 cartridge paper folded in half. The front of your folder should clearly show your name, your CDT group and the title of the project. This could be attractively drawn (for example using pictorial lettering) and could include a simple design.

Each sheet of paper should have a heading. The **brief, specification, research** and **evaluation** will consist mainly of writing, and can usually be done on file paper. The other sheets will contain mainly sketches, notes, working drawings or illustrations. These can be done on cartridge paper, bank paper, coloured paper or card as appropriate.

If the project involves making a model, a folder will still be needed for all your notes, sketches and drawings.

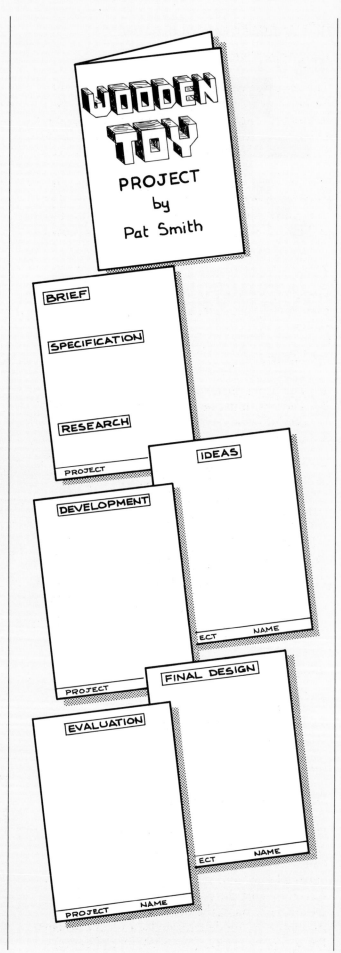

Model zoetrope

Background information

The zoetrope was one of the first attempts (in 1834) to make a moving picture machine. By looking through the slots of the rotating drum at the picture strip, you see each picture rapidly in succession. This makes them appear to move.

The picture strips can be changed, so you can draw as many moving pictures as you like. The movement must always repeat, for example, a child on a swing, a ball bouncing up and down.

Brief

Design and make a working model zoetrope using card, glue, plasticene, a paper clip and poster paint.

Specification

1   The drum must spin freely.
2   The base must be heavy so the machine will not fall over.
3   ... ? (continue)

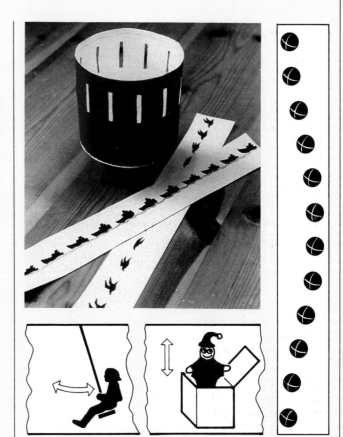

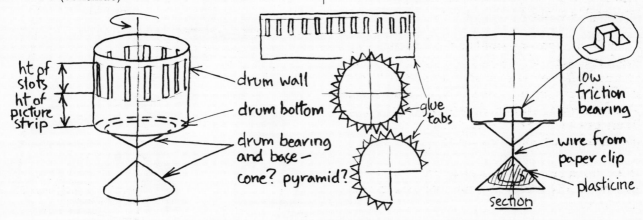

Research

1   How many slots should there be?
2   How wide should the slot be?
3   ... ? (continue)

Ideas

Development and final model

Draw full size developments of all the parts on card.
Cut these out, preferably using a craft knife, cutting board and steel ruler.
Carefully glue the parts together as required.
Decorate or paint the drum.
Assemble the model and make any adjustments.
Draw a picture strip (use bold, black shapes).

Evaluation

Does the model work properly? If not, can you put it right?
What difference does it make to the pictures if you shine a light into the top of the drum?
How does the width of the slots affect the picture?
What happens if the number of frames on the picture strip is one more, or one less than the number of slots?

Car dashboard

Background information

A car driver can glance at the dashboard for only a fraction of a second. Information must be displayed very clearly.

Much of the information a driver needs is about **quantities**: speed, remaining fuel, engine temperature, etc.

Quantities can be displayed in **analogue** form or **digital** form. An analogue watch, for example, has hands and a clock face. A digital watch shows digits only.

Digital displays are cheap to make, but they do not have the visual impact of analogue displays. Why is this?

One way to overcome this problem is to have a line of digital lights like the fuel gauge shown. This idea is used on audio equipment to show the volume of sound.

The British Standards Institution (BSI) recommend standard symbols to use for vehicle indicators. Most car manufacturers now use these.

Brief

Using the dashboard outline shown below, design a car dashboard to show the following displays:

- speed in mph
- remaining fuel in gallons
- current mpg (miles per gallon)
- coolant temperature in °C.

The dashboard must also show warning lights, with standard BSI symbols, for:

- indicator flashing left
- indicator flashing right
- headlights on full beam
- seat belt not fastened
- battery not being charged
- low engine oil pressure.

Produce a full size illustration of your final design.

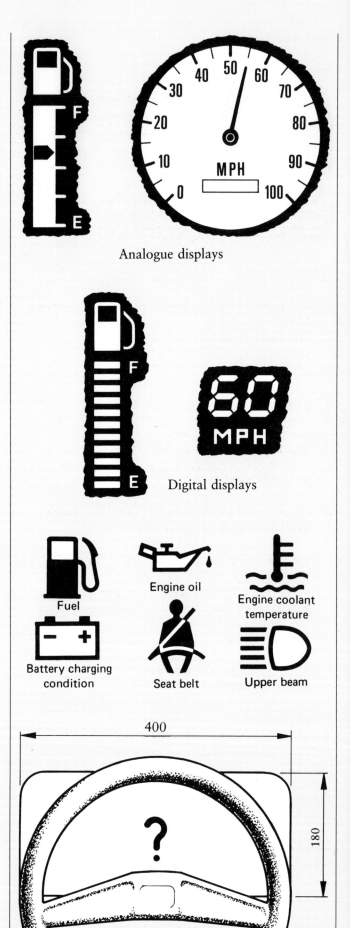

Analogue displays

Digital displays

Fuel

Engine oil

Engine coolant temperature

Battery charging condition

Seat belt

Upper beam

400

180

?

Specification

1 All the information must be clearly displayed at a glance.
2 The dashboard must have a pleasing appearance.
3 ... ? (continue)

Research

1 Collect illustrations and photographs of dashboards from manufacturers' catalogues. Everyone in your CDT group could contribute to a wall display.

2 Study and make sketches of car dashboards. Think about these questions:

  • Which display is usually the largest? Why is this?
  • Where is this display usually positioned?
  • Why are most dashboard layouts symmetrical?
  • Where are colours used? What do they mean?
  • Are most dashboards light or dark in colour? Why?

Ideas

Sketch in colour several ideas for each of the displays.
Sketch several ideas for the layout of the dashboard. Use bank paper over a square grid and sketch half full size.

Include in your sketches the best ideas from your research.

Development

Which are your best ideas? Ask at least one experienced driver for their opinion. Make notes about any changes you intend to make, and why.

Does the steering wheel hide any important information? A steering wheel shape made from card could be used to test this.

Final illustration

Use sugar paper or card of your chosen background colour. Draw and cut out the full size shape of the dashboard.

Draw and colour the displays and warning lights on cartridge paper. Cut out and mount them on the dashboard in the chosen position.

Evaluation

Compare and discuss your final designs. Do they match up to the original specifications? What do adult drivers think?

Housing estate

Background information

Housing estates vary a great deal, according to when and where they were built. New houses tend to be set well back from the road. This gives them a spacious appearance when seen from the road, but the back gardens can be small.

Twelve new semi-detached houses, similar to those shown at the bottom of the page, are to be built as part of a new housing estate. A plan of the site is shown below.

The builders need an accurate site plan showing each house and plot boundary. They would also like to advertise the houses to potential customers.

Brief

Design a suitable layout for six plots and houses on the given site, including a suitable access road. Produce:

● a site plan to a scale of 1:500
● a pictorial illustration of the completed site.

Specification

1 The plots should all be about the same area.
2 The finished environment should be pleasant, attractive and safe.
3 ... ? (continue)

Research

Compare different housing estates in your area. Collect photographs of street scenes from, for example, newspapers. What facilities are there? What facilities should there be? What do your friends thinks?

Ideas

Draw the site outline to a scale of 1:500 on A4 cartridge paper. Sketch several layouts of the site on bank paper laid over this drawing.

Development

Choose your best layout, and state your reasons for choosing it. Add any improvements you want to make, for example, planting new trees.

Final drawings

Complete the site plan by drawing accurately each house outline, the plot boundaries and any new features you have decided to add.

Draw a pictorial view in isometric projection, to the same scale, on A3 cartridge paper. It should be coloured and made as realistic as possible.

Evaluation

Compare and discuss your finished designs. Given the choice of these, where would **you** live, and why?

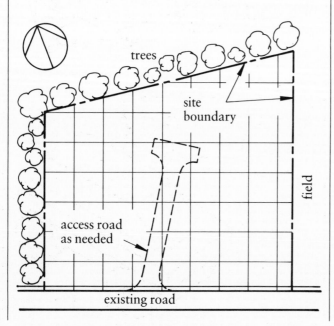

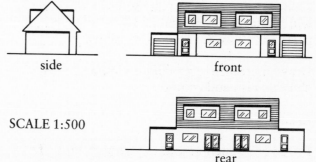

SCALE 1:500

The houses to be built (scale 1:500)

Wooden toy

Background information

A manufacturer of wooden toys for young children is looking for a new range of designs for toy vehicles.

To keep production simple and costs down, the manufacturer wants to use the range of wood sections and wheels shown. Ideas could include tractors, trains, trucks, cars, moon vehicles.

Brief

Design a toy vehicle using the given wood sections and wheels. The ends can be shaped as required. Produce a working drawing and a pictorial illustration of the finished toy.

Specification

1   The toy must be appealing to a young child.
2   ... ? (continue)

Research

1   Collect or look at similar toys from shops or home.
2   Colour and finish – varnish? stain? paint?
3   ... ? (continue).

Ideas

The most detailed view of a vehicle is usually the side view, so sketch side views of several ideas for a vehicle design. Colour or shade your sketches.

Development

Select your best idea and state on your sketch why you have selected it. Sketch an oblique or isometric view. Make any changes you think are necessary.

Final drawings

Produce a full size working drawing – two views will probably be enough. Draw up an item list of parts and show the main dimensions.

Draw an isometric or oblique view and show the chosen finish and colour.

Evaluation

Does your design appeal to young children, for example, your younger brother or sister? Perhaps you could ask them.

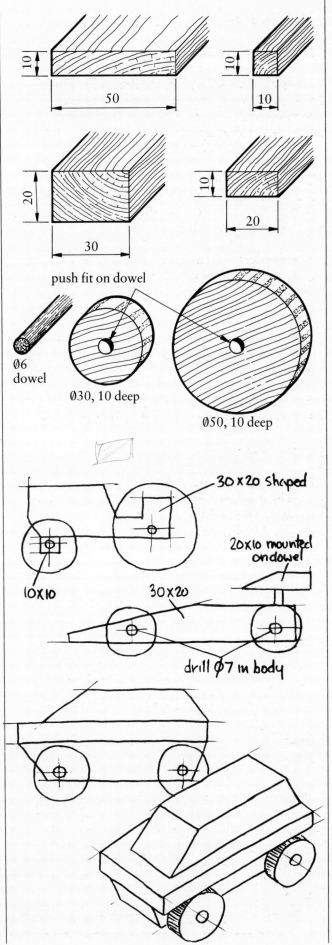

push fit on dowel

Ø6 dowel

Ø30, 10 deep

Ø50, 10 deep

30 x 20 shaped

20 x 10 mounted on dowel

10 x 10

30 x 20

drill Ø7 in body

Kitchen design

Background information

A kitchen is a kind of workshop. More work probably gets done there than in any other room in the house! Like any workshop, it should be easy and safe to work in.

But a kitchen is also a room for living in, so it should be a pleasant environment. Few people would want their kitchen to look like a garage workshop.

The drawing opposite shows some kitchen layouts. Which one is used depends on the shape of the room, and how much storage and worktop area is needed.

Brief

Design a kitchen layout for the room below, using the units shown. Produce a plan and a pictorial illustration of the finished layout. Extra worktops can be fitted as needed.

Specification

1 The finished kitchen should be easy to use (ergonomic).
2 The finished kitchen should be safe.
3 . . . ? (continue)

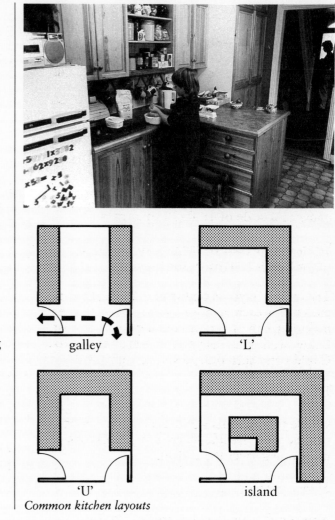

Common kitchen layouts
galley   'L'
'U'   island

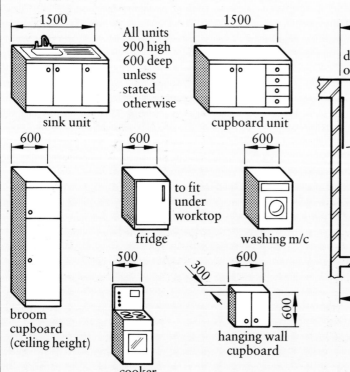

1500
sink unit

1500
cupboard unit

All units 900 high 600 deep unless stated otherwise

600
broom cupboard (ceiling height)

600
fridge — to fit under worktop

600
washing m/c

500
cooker

300 / 600 / 600
hanging wall cupboard

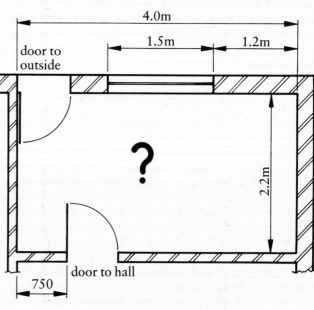

4.0m
1.5m
1.2m
door to outside
2.2m
door to hall
750

Outside walls are 250 thick
Inside walls are 100 thick
Doors are 750 wide
Ceiling is 2.3m from floor

Research

1   How can cooker fumes be extracted?
2   How can the cupboard space in the corners of the room be used? How is this done in your kitchen?
3   What is the best height to fix the hanging wall cupboards?
4   . . . ? (continue)

Ideas

Draw the plan of the room on 5mm square grid paper to a scale of 1:20 (10 squares = 1m).

Draw and cut out rectangles from card to represent plan views of the units.

Try various layouts on the plan using the card pieces. For each layout imagine, for example, making a cup of tea, or cooking eggs on toast. Draw 'walk lines' as you move around the room. Could you shorten the distance you walk?

Development

Check your layouts against each point of your specification. Decide where extra worktops are needed (e.g. over the fridge).

Final drawings

You could draw the plan and an isometric illustration on one A3 sheet side by side. Draw a 'ghosted' isometric outline of the room using very thin lines. Draw your units in the chosen positions and colour them.

Evaluation

Compare and discuss your finished designs. Do you drawings show all the necessary information?

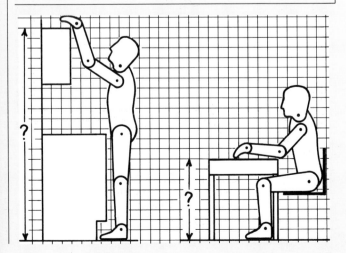

Make this design aid model

This 1:10 scale adult figure is a useful design aid for this project, and for designing furniture or seating where human use (ergonomics) is important. You can use the model as a template and trace around it in any position, on either side.

Trace each part of the model separately, transfer them all on to stiff card and cut them out. Use a hole punch to make a Ø5 hole at each joint. Fix the joints loosely using eyelets and eyelet pliers.

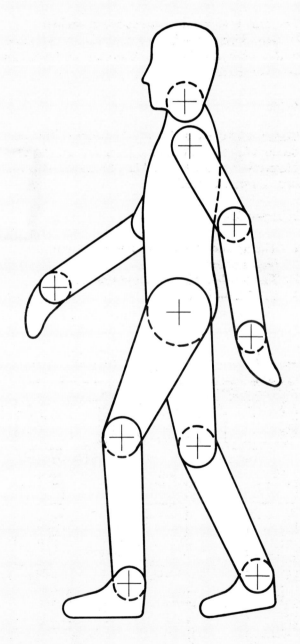

Further project ideas

1 **Brief**: A new shop selling games and puzzles has opened in your town. The owner would like you to:

- Think of a name for the shop.
- Design a suitable letter style and logo for the shop name.
- Produce a model carrier bag with the shop name and logo on it.
- Design an advertisement for the local paper.

2 **Brief**: A cycling magazine wants you to draw a coloured illustration to show how a bicycle pump works.

Take a bicycle pump apart and examine the parts. Why is the air pushed one way but not the other? Measure the parts for your drawing. This could show a section through the pump with all the parts labelled. Add a written description 'How a bicycle pump works'.

3 **Brief**: Design and make a model of a lampshade for a ceiling light which can be sold as a flat pack, using card and string only.

The specification should mention ventilation, appearance, and colour. For your research you could examine how existing lampshades are made, how they look and how the light is shed.

4 **Brief**: Design a 3-D (3 × 3 × 3) noughts and crosses game to be made from clear acrylic sheet.

You need to think about appearance, and ease of access to all the positions on each level. You could use coloured pegs to represent noughts and crosses.

5 **Brief**: Design a breadboard which would make it possible for a one handed person to slice the bread. (There are a large number of handicapped people with only one usable hand.)

You will need need some sort of adjustable clamp to hold various sizes of loaf. The clamp must need only one hand to operate it!

6 **Brief**: A shoe manufacturer wants a report comparing the various ways of fastening shoes:

laces, buckles, elastic (slip-on), velcro, flip-flops

Draw up tables or charts which state what you think are the advantages and disadvantages of each. Can you think of ways of testing these? Each method should be illustrated, either by drawings or by cuttings from advertisements or catalogues.

Perhaps you can invent a revolutionary new method of fastening shoes?

7 **Brief**: Prepare a report showing whether pupils are eating a healthy diet in the school canteen.

Conduct a survey amongst pupils from each year group. You need to think of a way of recording how much they eat of each food. You also need to find out how much carbohydrates, fat, protein, etc. each food contains. Where could you get this information?

Include bar charts and other charts as necessary in your final report. What are you conclusions?

8 Prepare your own brief based on a hobby or a topic you find interesting or worthwhile.

Ask your teacher for his or her opinion before starting any design work.